P9-CEM-381

THOMAS WILLIS

1621 - 1675

Portrait of Thomas Willis. As it appears in Collected Works. Amsterdam 1682–After an engraving by David Loggan (1666). – Institute of the History of Medicine, Zürich.

THOMAS WILLIS
1621-1675
Doctor and Scientist

by

Dr. Hansruedi Isler

with 11 illustrations

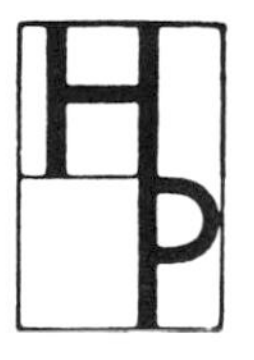

HAFNER PUBLISHING COMPANY
New York - London
1 9 6 8

English Edition, First Printing, 1968

Translated by the author with several additions
from the original German edition,
Band 29 of Grosse Naturforscher, published by
Wissenschaftliche Verlagsgesellschaft m.b.H., Stuttgart, 1965

Printed and Published by
Hafner Publishing Company, Inc.
31 East 10th Street
New York, N.Y. 10003

Library of Congress Catalog Card Number: 67-25769

Printed in U.S.A. by
NOBLE OFFSET PRINTERS, INC.
NEW YORK 3, N. Y.

TABLE OF CONTENTS

INTRODUCTION

Historians are, like most mortals, rather unsystematic and subject to fashion. Certain great figures of the past are discussed by them over and over again. Others, hardly less important, are neglected or forgotten. This habit becomes particularly annoying in a field like the history of science and medicine, which counts a relatively limited number of devotees. In the case of British medical history of the 17th century, for decades the interest of historians has been concentrated on WILLIAM HARVEY and THOMAS SYDENHAM and the numerous other outstanding figures of that most brilliant period have not be considered. Probably the greatest of these forgotten men is THOMAS WILLIS. It gives me therefore great pleasure to introduce the Anglosaxon readers to the first monograph on Willis which has just been authored by a very gifted young Swiss physician-scholar, Doctor Hansruedi Isler. Dr. Isler is an excellent linguist and has practiced his art in the mountains of Nepal as well as in those of Switzerland.

Dr. Isler's monograph gives a vivid picture of Willis' life, of his progress from a poor peasant boy to the most affluent practitioner of London. Willis life span (1621-75) coincides with the eventful decades, which saw the rise of the first British settlements in North America and the

English revolution, during which Willis was a kind of royalist underground fighter.

Dr. Isler surveys the very extensive scientific accomplishments of Willis, today best known in the field of neuroanatomy, neurophysiology and neuropathology. It should not be overlooked that they were preceded by great descriptions of epidemic diseases, and chemical ideas on health and disease, which included astonishing premonitions of internal secretion. The author is never forgetful of the fact that Willis, great as he was, was but the member of a group, of that of the "vertuosi," the founders of the Royal Society. He deals with the paradox, that this political reactionary was a scientific revolutionary, and explains, why this man, so very influential during his lifetime, was later so quickly forgotten. Not the least merit of this book is that it dispenses with a great number of legends (Sylvius' influence on Willis; Sydenham's independence of him etc.).

Its greatest virtue is that it sees always Willis' work as a whole and not as an agglomeration of discoveries, and that it always sees it in the framework of his time.

ERWIN H. ACKERKNECHT, M.D.

Zürich, May 1967

PREFACE

Every medical student knows about the Circle of Willis. But he hardly ever knows anything about the man whose name he thus uses, nor about his accomplishments. This holds good even for many students of medical history, and it is not astonishing, since textbooks and manuals of the history of medicine contain only scanty information about Thomas Willis and his works.

Yet Willis is responsible for decisive changes in various medical fields; medicine as a whole owes very much to his ideas. His influence was of particular importance in the development of epidemiology and nosology, biochemistry, anatomy and physiology of the nervous system, neuropathology, psychopathology, pharmacology, and therapeutics.

His first book (1659) initiated the great tradition of systematic nosology and epidemiology that was later continued by Sydenham and Morton. Willis proclaimed the paramount importance of critical direct observation in medicine. The same method enabled him to discover new diseases, like myasthenia gravis, new syndromes, like Paracusis Willisii, and new signs, such as the sweetness of diabetic urine.

In biochemistry he formulated a theory of fermentation that was to become the basis of most of the reasonable explanations of fermentative phenomena up to the nineteenth century. Willis was the first to recognize the biological importance of protein, and he first described in detail the effects of what he thought was a living ferment—the secondary effects of the sexual hormones. He concluded from evidence that this ferment was able to change the course of a disease.

Willis' achievements in neuroanatomy and neurophysiology comprise the first useful theory of brain localization of psychic and vegetative functions as well as the first interpretation of nerve action as an energetic process. His new concept of nerve action led him to the idea—and the term—of reflex action, whereas his localization theory gave rise to the development of experimental physiology of the central nervous system. In order to complete his account of the nervous system Willis described the bulk of the nervous and psychic diseases: the three books he published from 1667 to 1672 contain the most complete text of neuropsychiatry since Greek antiquity. Most later interpretations of psychophysical relationships have been influenced by his ideas, either directly or indirectly.

"Pharmaceutice Rationalis," his last book, was a serious attempt to establish pharmacology as a science based upon anatomy, morbid anatomy, animal experiments, chemistry, and the best medical knowledge then available. Besides, it contains many descriptions of diseases which are of great value. Willis contributed much to the general acceptance of quinine therapy; it has been said that he reintroduced the colchicine therapy of gout.

This list is far from complete, since it is only intended to give a preliminary impression; but the historical significance of Willis' works as a whole should not be omitted. His books contain a system of his own, a baroque edifice of thoughts built up from Paracelsian chemistry, Baconian experimental science, the Harveian innovation, and a profound knowledge of ancient medical authors. After the discredit of the Galenic system, this ingenious synthesis of knowledge, scientific methods, and bold ideas provided a new groundwork for the following generations of physicians, and it certainly helped to shape their way of scientific thinking.

Notwithstanding these great merits, no book and no paper gives an adequate picture of Willis and his work. as a whole. It is only in some publications devoted to special problems that his achievements have received due attention: in Canguilhem's "Formation of the Concept of Reflex" (111), in Neuburger's "Historical Development of Experimental Physiology of the Brain and Spinal Cord . . ." (117), and in Jules Soury's classic "Central Nervous Systems" (105). More recently Alfred Meyer and Raymond Hierons (108, 182, 198-201) have published a series of papers containing precise answers to several selected questions arising from Willis' neurological work. Finally, in 1965 appeared Feindel's delightful facsimile edition of Willis' "Anatomy of the Brain," accompanied by a volume of valuable information about Willis, his friends and the "Anatomy." (198).

Apart from the remaining lack of good overall evaluation, many opinions about Willis are extremely controversial. C. C. Mettler, for instance, thought that Willis was something of a dandy who managed to get the credit for the work of others, whereas Jules Soury could only compare him to Shakespeare for his profundity and his superb Latin style.

Willis' life was a most interesting one in a highly interesting period of political, religious, cultural, and scientific history. As biographical data is scarce, his background must help to complete the picture. Willis was the teacher of men like Robert Hooke, John Locke, and Richard Lower. The greatest of English architects, Christopher Wren, was his research assistant, and drew illustrations for his brain anatomy. Willis belonged to the founders of the Royal Society. This calls for a brief account of these men. The fact that Willis managed to be a loyal partisan to several antagonistic groups and factions at the same time must be further explained by means of brief descriptions of the controversial tendencies that moved England during the Civil War, the Commonwealth, and the Restoration.

In the present investigation I have attempted to outline how Willis lived, what he wrote, what he achieved, why his fame vanished. I hope that this book will help to restore him to his rightful place in the history of medicine, science, and thought, contributing thus to the better understanding of a great period in which English supremacy in medicine developed simultaneously with England's rise to world power.

THOMAS WILLIS

1621 - 1675

I. THE LIFE AND TIMES OF WILLIS

Thomas Willis was born on January 27th, 1621, in Great Bedwyn, Wiltshire, England. (1, 2, 3, 4) There is some disagreement as to the status of his father, Thomas Willis. Wood (4a, cf. 1) says that he was "... of North Hinxsey, yeoman, sometimes butler to Sir George Stonehouse of Radley, afterwards baillive of the mannor of Great Bedwin in Wilts, belonging to Sir Walter Smith (at which place Dr. Thomas Willis was borne) ." In Munk's "Roll of the R. C. P." we read that he was "a farmer at Church or Long Handborough" before coming to Great Bedwyn. (88) John Fell, Willis' brother-in-law, says in a postscript to "Pharmaceutice Rationalis" (24), that the elder Willis had graduated Master of Arts in Oxford. This has been denied by Wood (1) and upheld by Willis' grandson, Browne Willis. (cf. 5) However, the elder Willis is not mentioned among the graduates in the "Alumni Oxonienses." (2) Wood (1) adds that in his last days he was "a constant Inhabitant of N. Henxsey," where he had, according to Fell, an estate. (24) His first wife, the mother of Dr. Willis, Rachel Howell by her maiden name, died in 1631. At that time Thomas was ten years old. (3, 4a)

References to his youth are very scarce. We know that, from North Hinksey, he went daily to the grammar school of Edward Sylvester in All Saints Parish in Oxford. (1, 5) To this Browne Willis adds an anecdote clearly intended as proof of his grandfather's kind heart. On his way to school, he relates, Willis would give away to the poor his provisions for the day. His father, fearing that the boy might go hungry, compelled him to eat all his food at home. (5)

In 1636 he was taken into service by Dr. Thomas Iles, a canon of Christ Church College, Oxford, "and was his batler there." (1, 3) He matriculated from Christ Church on March 3rd, 1636/7. (2) As a batler or batteler, he was a member of the lowest class of students.* According to Aubrey (169), he ". . . was first servitor to Dr. Iles, one of the Canons of Christ Church, whose wife was a knowing woman in physic and surgery, and did many cures. Tom Willis then wore a blue livery cloak and studied at the lower end of the hall, by the hall dore; was pretty handy, and his mistresse would oftentimes have him to assist her in making of medicines. This did him no hurt, and allured him on."

* In seventeenth-century England students were classed as follows (7):

1. pensionarii maiores: fellow commoners, gentlemen commoners.
2. pensionarii minores: commoners.
   The pensionarii paid for their board and lodging.
3. pauperes scholares, mediastini: sizars, servitors, batlers or battelers.
   They were supported by college funds or by their masters.

About that time Christ Church College housed 8 canons, 8 chapter-clerks, 8 musicians, 8 choristers, 101 students, a great number of assistants and servitors and 24 paupers in the poorhouse nearby. The college was so crowded that its heads had trouble to obey Royal mandates for the admission of students. (9d) The batlers and servitors often lived in utter poverty. (8, 9a, b, c) As servants of persons of rank they were at least entitled to gather the leftovers from their masters' tables. (8) Quarrels between members of the lowest class were frequent, especially between the servants of the canons and those of the gentlemen commoners. (9e)

Before taking up theology, medicine, or law, the students had to go through a complete course in the Liberal Arts and to take the degree of M.A. (11, 67) The subjects of these studies were prescribed by the so-called Laudian or Caroline Code, the constitution of the University of Oxford, ratified in 1636, and valid up to the nineteenth century. (11, 12a) They comprised, among others, grammar, rhetorics, dialectics, moral philosophy, natural philosophy, geometry, astronomy, metaphysics, and music. (11b) The students were trained to dispute in Latin according to very strict rules. The logic to be used in these disputations was that of Aristotle, "whose authority shall be supreme." (11c) The philosophical doctrine had to be made to conform to theological truth. (11d) The scholastic regulations of the Code were obeyed to the letter. (12d) In the disputations the same problems were perpetually harped on. The candidates for the master's degree had to defend their thesis in that way for four days. Essentially the University was still a medieval school for the clergy, the methods of teaching were scholastic (13a), and "the authority of Aristotle was to be paramount within the whole sphere of his voluminous writings." (13b)

Young Thomas Willis, applying himself very severely to his studies (1), was thus educated in the medieval tradition. He received the same form of training that animated John Locke to read the wordy romances of his day instead of the texbooks, and that bored Thomas Hobbes so terribly that he preferred to go and bait jackdaws with lime-strings and cheese. (3) Exuberance of wits does not seem to have been very popular in this environment: by "shewing himself too forward, pragmatical and conceited" one could expect to be "often kick'd and beaten," as was the case with the pamphleteer Henry Stubbe, who came from humble origins. (1)

When Willis came to Oxford, Bacon, Gilbert and Harvey had long ago published their books containing the essential ideas of the *New* or experimental science. The very foundations of the great Aristotelian system had already been undermined by Ramus, Gassendi, and Descartes. In spite of this the new way of thinking did not exert much influence in Oxford. (12a, b, 13a, 14b, d, 18) The university men were kept under close control by the officials and the tutors. Unfortunately, nothing is known of Willis' tutors, and next to nothing about his teachers. But there was a heterogeneous and widespread movement; its revolutionary ideas reached almost everybody underhand. To the followers of Paracelsus the carefully guarded monopoly of traditional learning was not impregnable: although their thoughts were shut out from lectures and disputations, they were introduced inconspicuously in the wake of chemical remedies and astrology.

The Paracelsists had begun to fight for the primacy of "palpable and visible experience" and against the "heathenish philosophy of Aristotle and Galen" even before Bacon. (16a, 109) Many Paracelsists were adepts of astrology, alchemy, and the Cabbala; of those the most famous was Dr. Robert Fludd (1574-1637), who devised a cosmic system of mystical medicine. Admiration for his work survived the victory of experimental science for many years, and such earnest philosophers as Gassendi and Descartes's friend Mersenne considered it worthy of extensive criticism. The mystical fields of knowledge were believed to be akin to the "New Science," and the pamphleteers, who after the Puritan victory fought for the introduction of experiments into the course of studies, often demanded to include alchemy and astrology. As late as 1654, Seth Ward, then professor of astronomy at Oxford, found it necessary to point out the antagonism between the teachings of Fludd and Bacon. (14c, 17) The majority of the Paracelsists were apothecaries, medical practitioners, and physicians, who relied upon chemical remedies instead of the botanical preparations used by Galenical medicine. The wife of Willis' master, Canon

Iles, was a medical practitioner and possibly a Paracelsist.

From their chemical activities, the Paracelsists were known as Chymists or Spagyrists. Other names bestowed on them were: Iatrochemists, Chemiatrists, or Helmontians or Willisians and the like, depending on what protagonist was most popular at a given time.

Robert Boyle mentions Jean Beguin, a French apothecary, as the leader of the Chymists. Beguin had set up an atomistic theory of matter. His manual of chemical technique (Tyrocinium chymicum, 1st ed. Paris, 1610) existed, at the time of Willis' matriculation, in sixteen Latin editions. Similar manuals were quite common in the first half of the seventeenth century. (19) The English apothecaries gradually managed to introduce the use of chemical remedies, as the successive editions of the Pharmacopoeia Londinensis show. (61)

The first edition was prepared under the supervision of Theodore Turquet de Mayerne, of Geneva; it contained some chemical prescriptions, such as calomel. Turquet, court physician in London at that time, was "a good chemist for his time." The popularity of chemical medicine in England was mostly due to Turquet and some other chemists of good repute, like the former pirate, Sir Kenelm Digby. (60a, b, c) It is highly probable that Willis, while assisting mistress Iles "in making of medicines," came to know chemical manuals or the Pharmacopoeia Londinensis, and thus became aware of chemical medicine.

In June 1643 the Civil War broke out. In the same month Willis graduated Master of Arts. (1, 2) The University was a Royalist stronghold from the beginning; as soon as in August, voluntaries for the King were enlisted. The King came to Oxford in late autumn and took up his residence in Christ Church College. (9e, 22, 23a) His physician in ordinary, William Harvey, followed him to Oxford. (3)

Willis joined the Royal voluntaries, who were instructed and trained on the University grounds. (1, 24) They were for the most part archers. (23a) Wood (in Boase, 164) says, that they soon were ". . . much debauched and become idle by their bearing arms and keeping company with rude soldiers. Much of their precious time was lost by being upon the guard night after night . . ." and they had opportunities of "gaming, drinking, swearing, &c . . . The truth is that they (I blame not all) were so guilty of those vices, that those that were looked upon as good wits, and of great parts at their first coming, were by strange inventions (not now to be named) to entice them to drinking and to be drunk, totally lost and rendered useless." But Wood (1) tells us that Willis was among the exceptions: ". . . he, among the Scholars that were then remaining, bore Arms in his (the King's) Defence, and all the time that he could obtain, he bestowed on his beloved Study of Physic."

In 1643, Willis' father died (4a) from "camp fever" (24) during an epidemic of which Willis gives such an accurate account in his book "Of Fevers" (25) that the diagnosis of typhus fever is beyond doubt. (59) Willis remembers that in several villages around Oxford the older people were completely exterminated, so that many old customs and privileges were forever lost.

His medical studies began in 1643. Medical education in the English Universities was so old-fashioned that many future physicians preferred to study on the Continent. It was also possible to evade the Universities by getting a doctor's degree from the Archbishop of Canterbury. Previous acquaintance with medical knowledge was not required in this procedure. (26) In Oxford the Regius Professor of Medicine was by statute bound to read from the works of Hippocrates or Galen every Tuesday and Friday morning at eight o'clock. (11f) The students had to follow these lectures for three years before taking the degree of bachelor of medicine. (11e) In order to get the licence to practice they had to prove that they had been present at a complete dissection and a complete lecture on the human skeleton. (11g) After having procured a corpse (usually that of a criminal, after the Lent assizes), the professor of anatomy was to have it dissected by a surgeon, demonstrating and explaining the different parts and their "site, nature, use and office." (11h) Except for these demonstrations, medical education consisted of readings in the classical books and formal disputations of their contents. In the disputations, subjects such as "whether it be possible to cure a disease by means of a disease" or "whether human life could endure without respiration" were treated during long hours in rooms that often remained nearly empty. (26)

From 1643 to 1646 the University suffered from the effects of the war. The school buildings were employed as granaries for the garrison, lectures and disputations were suspended in most cases, and graduations grew scarce. (13d) Moreover, after the typhus epidemic, Oxford was ravaged by a fire that destroyed about three hundred and thirty houses. (164) We must assume that Willis' medical education was, at least for the greater part, that of an autodidact.

In that time Harvey's discovery of the circulation of the blood, which he had published years ago, was finally introduced into Oxford by its author. Harvey lived in Oxford from 1642 to 1646, and there demonstrated the circulation of the blood in a live dog, an exploit duly praised in the *carmen de sanguinis circuitu* in Latin verse by the otherwise unknown poet Robert Grove. (28, 29) In 1645 Harvey was appointed Warden of Merton, and thus became a member of the University hierarchy. Under these circumstances it must have become difficult for the University to ignore his teachings any longer.

In April 1646 the King fled from Oxford. In June the fortress was surrendered to the rebel forces. The revolutionaries were for the greater part of Puritan conviction: they detested the medieval clerical tradition. The majority of the University men were Royalists and deeply rooted in this tradition.

In December 1646 Thomas Willis graduated bachelor of medicine and received the licence to practice. (1, 2) He "fell to the practice of it, and every monday kept Abingdon Market . . . So that by his great Care and industry he in short time became famous in these Parts, settled in St. John Baptist's Parish, in an House opposite to Merton Coll. Church, and was sent for far and near for his help . . ." (1) There is evidence that this house, Beam Hall in Merton Street, was quite sumptuous in comparison with most other Oxford houses: in 1665, he paid eight shilling "Hearth Tax," which was not imposed upon houses below twenty shilling annual value, amounting to two shilling per fireplace; the same document shows that about ninety-five per cent of Oxford citizens paid less than six shilling, and that, besides Willis, only one *doctor* lived outside the colleges.* (171)

Towards the end of 1647 the rebels began a purge in order to clear Oxford from the more fanatic among the Royalists. They appointed the Parliamentary Visitors who ejected all those not willing to swear an oath of allegiance to Parliament.

They prohibited the Anglican ritual because of its medieval and Catholic traits. The use of the Common Prayer Book in churches and chapels was suppressed. Traditional services were not to be held any more. The spiritual center of the University, the Cathedral of the

* The house is still in existence. For a photograph of its recent state see Feindel (107). An earlier drawing is reproduced on page 241, below. For a 17th century drawing see Dewhurst. (175)

See of Oxford, which was also the college chapel of Christ Church, was thus bereft of its religious life. To this outrage the pious Anglicans could never resign themselves. Three clergymen who had been ejected from Christ Church College, John Fell, John Dolben, and Richard Allestree, continued the forbidden services in secret, at first in Thomas Willis' rooms in Christ Church, and soon afterwards in his house, Beam Hall. His part in this underground movement has earned Willis a place of honor in English history. (1, 3, 4, 9, 13, 22, 23, 24) His marriage to the sister of one of the three divines, John Fell, possibly was a further consequence of this involvement. Since Willis was not ejected by the Visitors, he must have taken the oath. In the register of the Visitors for October 1648 he is mentioned among "such as are chosen into Colledges." (31) His former master, Canon Iles, was removed from the College, lost his title, position, and money, and died in misery in 1649. (2)

The interference of the Puritans in the University was responsible for the decisive change in Willis' environment. In 1648 several prominent members of the movement for experimental science were appointed to Oxford chairs. (16k, 34) They belonged to the group which Robert Boyle called "the Invisible College." At Gresham College in London they had begun to put into practice the theories of Francis Bacon's "Novum Organon" and "De Augmentis Scientiarum." They had attempted to lay the foundations of a new natural philosophy out of "palpable and visible experience."

Now they were set up in leading University positions, and this was clearly intended as a further blow against the clerical tradition, since one of their aims was to pull down a cornerstone of the old teachings, the natural philosophy of Aristotle. Puritan ethics demanded that men spend their time profitably. (34) The Puritans regarded the Universities as places of idle sophistication, and philosophy and metaphysics as unprofitable arts. From experimental science they expected technical improvements useful for the "common wealth." (16k)

Among the *natural philosophers* from London the most noted were two mathematicians and divines, John Wilkins, John Wallis, and the "chemical doctor" Jonathan Goddard, who had been professor of medicine at Gresham College, Seth Ward, who brought the teachings of Copernicus to Oxford, and William Petty. They were joined by Robert Boyle, who set up his private laboratory in Oxford. This gathering of outstanding students included also Christopher Wren, Charles Morton, and Laurence Rooke. (12c) Oxford became the center of the *New Science* in England. (16k) In his "History of the Royal Society" of 1667 (33) Thomas Sprat writes of the members of this group that they "had begun a free way of reasoning." (33a) They used to meet in Wilkins' or Petty's lodgings to discuss the experiments and theories of their *natural philosophy*. They dealt with many aspects of nature. (14f) Contrary to the doctrine of their ideologist, Francis Bacon, their research often depended upon hypotheses which they wished to prove. (14g, 35) Primarily, they thought of the possible practical uses of their discoveries. (14i, 16, 34) As one of the most important and most constant of these researchers, Sprat mentions Thomas Willis, then "an eminent physician in Oxford." (33a) "These persons," says Wood (16d), "gave themselves the name of Vertuosi and pretended to go beyond all others in the University for knowledge, which causing envy in many, some, especially those of the old stamp, that had been eminent for School and Polemical Divinity, and other polite parts of Learning, looked upon them very inconsiderably, and their Experiments as much below their profund Learning and the Professors of them. Undervalued by the Aristotlelians, Galenists, profound disputants and schoolmen, who looked upon their operation as much below their philosophy, and rather to be embraced by the Quack Salvers and Apothecaries boys than by them . . ." The *Vertuosi* contended that the University "slavishly tie up its Youth to the magisterial Dictates of Aristotle" (Wood, 32), whereas the Aristotelians frequently brought the charge of irrationality against the men who tended to trust "rather in deluding experiments, than in rational arguments." (14e) Attempts made by the *Vertuosi* to placate this antagonism were of no avail, as they could not be expected to abstain from opposing the authority of tradition. (cf. 16d)

In 1647 Sir Thomas Clayton had taken his father's place as professor of medicine and anatomy at Oxford. (36a) He managed to get hold of a handful of appointments and honors. (36b) But Sir Thomas, "being possess'd with a timorous and effeminate Humour, could never endure the sight of a mangled or bloody Body." (37) The students made fun of him. A poem of theirs has been handed down to us in which he is accused of having mistaken the liver for the heart. (38a) At last he followed the advice of the unknown poet and gave up "trading in blood." He appointed William Petty as his deputy, and in 1650 wholly renounced the chair of anatomy.

Petty was unanimously elected professor of anatomy in Clayton's place. As befits a true *Vertuoso,* he was also elected Gresham Professor of Music three months later. In Oxford he "followed the Faculty of Physic, exercised Anatomy and Chymistry much among young Scholars . . ." (37) and "cut up doggs" (27), that is, performed experiments upon live animals. Furthermore he advanced several ingenious schemes for the improvement of education, directed the survey of Ireland for the Commonwealth, and nearly succeeded in introducing a new type of ship into the Navy. He had constructed and launched a kind of catamaran, a "double-bottomed ship" with two parallel hulls connected by a platform, and armed with fifty guns. It was christened "The Experiment" by King Charles II, and much admired even in France. (156, 163) In the twentieth century similar constructions have been found to sail exceptionally well (172), but Petty's prototype was shipwrecked in a storm in which a great number of conventional vessels also perished, and the conservatism of the Navy prevented further experiments. (1, Petty) Petty was one of the foremost promotors of the

New Science (16c), and it is most likely that he was the one to acquaint Thomas Willis with it: Petty's activity in Oxford covered much the same subjects as that of Willis, and Willis worked in close association with him as early as 1650 or 1651 (see below p. 18).

Petty's great versatility was no exception among the *Vertuosi,* who endeavoured to be universally "philosophic in mind." (36b, 37, 38a, 38e) Wren and Hooke, for example, were prodigies of at least the same magnitude; both were temporarily Willis' associates. Christopher Wren assisted Dr. Charles Scarborough in his lectures at Surgeons' Hall, where he made anatomical demonstrations and preparations and performed various experiments. He took part in the research for Willis' "Anatomy of the Brain" and drew most of the illustrations for the book. In 1663 Boyle mentions Wren as the inventor of the "Experiment, of taking out the Spleen of a dog without killing him . . ." (38e) In 1657 Wren was appointed professor of astronomy in London, and in 1661 at Oxford. Pascal was much impressed by Wren's mathematical prowess, as was Isaac Newton, who called him a prince "among the geometers of this age." (159) His achievements in architecture are still famous. After the Great Fire he built St. Paul's Cathedral and designed the fifty-one parochial churches then reconstructed in London. Although his great plan for rebuilding the whole city was not realized, he succeeded in leaving London with the indelible mark of a creative effort that is almost beyond comparison. (159, 46)

In 1650 (27) or 1651 (173) William Petty and Thomas Willis became famous in a rather peculiar way. For their anatomical dissections they received the body of one Anne Green, who had been hanged for murdering her illegitimate child. What happened to her is related as follows: ". . . to the place of Execution: where after singing of a Psalme and something said in justification of herself, as to the fact for which she was to suffer and touching the Lewdness of the Family wherein she lately lived, she was turn'd off the Ladder, hanging by the neck for the space of almost halfe an houre, some of her friends in the meantime thumping her on the breast, others hanging with all their weight upon her leggs, sometimes lifting her up, and then pulling her downe againe with a sudden jerke, thereby the sooner to dispach her out of her only paine, insomuch that the Under-Sheriffe fearing lest thereby they should breake the rope, forbad them to do so any longer. At length when every one thought she was dead, the body being taken downe, and put into a Coffin, was carried thence into a private House, where some Physitians had appointed to make a Dissection. The Coffin being open she was observed to breath and in breathing (the passage of her throat being streightned) obscurely to rattle. A young man standing by thought to put her out of her misery by stamping on her. Dr. Petty of Brasenose, our anatomy professor, and Mr. Thomas Willis of Christ Church perceiving some life in her, as well for humanity as for their Profession sake, fell presently to act in order to her recovery . . ." ("Newes from the Dead," 173). According to Evelyn (163), they "let bloud, put to bed to a warme woman, & with spirits & other meanes recovered her to life; The Young Scholars joyn'd & made her a little portion, married her to a Man who had severall children by her, living 15 yeares after, as I have been assured . . ."

The abolishment of the Aristotelian system by the *Vertuosi* had left a gap that Bacon's ideas could not fill. They were in need of a philosophical background. Among the *modern* philosophical systems, that of Pierre Gassendi (1592-1655) resembled that of the Aristotelians more closely than that of Descartes: it was founded upon the philosophy of Epicurus and Democritus (41), and it may well be considered the last serious attempt of *ancient* learning to cope with the new results of the experimental methods. Gassendi had introduced into philosophy the atomistic theory of matter, which had never been quite extinct since Epicurus. This theory had been renewed before in the corpuscular explanations which the chymists had found to fit their results. (20) Gassendi believed that the atoms moved in empty space, but empty space can be neither substance nor attribute: his theory showed all too clearly the shortcomings of the ancient system of categories by transcending it. (41e) In the meetings of the *Vertuosi* Gassendi's natural philosophy was often discussed and compared to that of Aristotle. (14h) Jones (16f) thinks that "Gassendi perhaps exerted more influence than any other foreigner upon the anti Aristotelian movement in England." Willis refers to him quite often, and some of his physical and physiological concepts, especially in "De Anima Brutorum," come from Gassendi.

Gassendi's philosophy had reached England through the emigrants returning home after the Civil War. (41b) Thomas Hobbes, the author of the "Leviathan," knew the important parts of the doctrine before their publication, and made them known among the emigrants. Together with Hobbes William Petty had studied anatomy in Paris. (21d) Antoine Adam (41c) says that Walter Charleton also was acquainted with the work of Gassendi through Hobbes. Charleton, court Physician to Charles I and Charles II, a distinguished member of the Royal College of Physicians, had studied in Oxford at about the same time as Willis. (3) In 1654 he published his "Physiologia* Epicuro-Gassendo-Charltoniana," in which he attempts to represent the whole field of contemporary *natural philosophy* and experimental science as seen by a follower of Gassendi. Charleton rejected any mathematical account of the arrangements of atoms as impossible. (14h) In general, the followers of Gassendi relied much less upon quantitative methods than the Cartesians.

In 1649 Richard Lower matriculated from Christ Church College. Soon afterwards he became assistant to Thomas Willis, helping him with his experiments, his dissections and his medical practice. Their relationship is sometimes explained like this: "Willis was con-

* In Charleton's title the word has its pre-Fernelian meaning of "science of nature" or "natural philosophy."

stantly suggesting research problems to Lower to see whether the experimental fact coincided with his own shrewd ideas . . ." (39) For the rest of his life, Lower was Willis' faithful disciple. When Willis moved to London sometime after 1666, Lower followed him and set up his practice there. Lower's "De Corde" of 1669 contains a remark that points to a slight cooling of their relationship (170), but there is no indication of a break between them. The way the public felt about their relationship seems to have been emphasized in a funeral elegy on Lower, printed as a broadsheet in 1691: (168)

> When the learn'd WILLIS dy'd, he did impart
> His utmost Skill to thy capacious Heart.
> Full well he knew, there was no other Shrine
> So fit to keep his Treasure in, as thine.
> So the old Seer did to his Son dispense,
> A double Portion of Prophetick Sense,
> When in his fiery Chair he mounted hence.
> WILLIS Expiring, joy'd in Thee, to find
> He'd such a Legacy for Human kind.
> A Legacy more valuable far,
> Than both the Indies and their Riches are.
> They cannot to our Days one Minute give;
> But Thousands by thy powerful Art still live.

In 1653 Robert Hooke was admitted to Christ Church College, where he earned his place as a chorister and a servitor to one Mr. Goodman. "The further course of his life," says Keynes (160), "was determined by his meeting . . . with Dr. Thomas Willis . . ." Willis made him his laboratory assistant, and later recommended him to Robert Boyle. (21c) Hooke became Boyle's technical assistant, and in this capacity invented and constructed most of the apparatus that enabled Boyle to perform his brilliant experiments. Through Willis and Boyle he was introduced to the other *Vertuosi,* and in 1662 he was appointed "Curator of Experiments" of the Royal Society they had founded.

Hooke was a universal genius like Petty and Wren. After the Great Fire of London he was made City Surveyor and took part in rebuilding the city, working in close association with his friend Wren. Hooke designed and built, among other edifices, the Royal College of Physicians and Bethlehem Hospital ("Bedlam"), both much admired while they stood, but pulled down in the nineteenth century. (160, 161) His claim to priority over Newton in the discovery of the law of gravitation has been supported by Aubrey. (21c) In 1665 he published his famous "Micrographia," the first treatise devoted mainly to microscopical observations. Also it represents most of the essential ideas of the pre-Newtonian *Vertuosi.* Its success was "immediate, widespread, and lasting." (161) In the preface Hooke refers to the great anatomists and their "excellent" work, namely, "Doctor Harvy, Doctor Ent, Doctor Willis, Doctor Glisson." (162) Hooke was appointed professor of geometry at Gresham College in 1666. In 1677 he became one of the two secretaries of the Royal Society. (160, 161) His inventions—mostly mechanical devices—he believed to be "not fewer than a thousand." (160) Like Leibniz and Flamsteed—for whom the Greenwich Observatory was built—he incurred the implacable enmity of Isaac Newton. This may, in part, account for the rapid dwindling of his fame after his death. (161)

We do not know much about Willis' practice in Oxford. Fortunately his clinical notebook of 1650 has been acquired by the Wellcome Historical Library; it is to be published soon. To judge from a preliminary report by Dewhurst (175) this notebook appears to be of great value because it proves that Willis' descriptions of diseases, and his biochemical observations, are results of his own experience. The first complete description of manic-depressive psychosis, the demonstration of the protein content of pleural exudate, and the discovery of the compensating function of the arterial anastomosis at the base of the brain, the circle of Willis, all go back to first-hand observations recorded in the early years of his practice.

Until his departure from Oxford Willis was often consulted by Lady Conway. In her letters (42) she wrote of him with considerable respect in spite of the fact that his treatment failed to help her. Lady Conway's case was as famous as it was hopeless: William Harvey, Sir Kenelm Digby, Turquet de Mayerne, and Robert Boyle, as well as quacks and faith-healers of all sorts had tried everything conceivable to rid her of her terrible headache, but to no avail. Harvey had at last recommended trephining. In his "De Anima Brutorum" Willis describes the case with great accuracy, as comparison with the Conway Letters (42) shows.

Willis' prescriptions were made by the apothecaries Hazlewood and Crosse. Crosse was also the landlord of Robert Boyle. Willis often used a syrup of sulphur, of which the Reverend John Ward wrote in his diary: (38) "Itt is his owne composition and no Apothecarie hath itt or knowes itt but ye two forementioned. Itt may be taken and is so usually with a Liquorish stick. It is a compound not above 4 d. an ounce, but it is most used in Colds and distempers of the Lungs." John Ward was a dilettante in medicine and experimental science. He was personally acquainted with Willis, and a friend and pupil of Lower. (38, 132) He tells us that Dr. Willis used to give more than 2½ oz. of quicksilver, because "ye more you give ye less is the danger. Itt does by its own weight passe quickly." (38c) However, Willis was aware of the hazards involved in this therapy; he strongly warned against the use of quicksilver without the strictest indication. (42, 57) He often prescribed salts of tartar, antimony, and iron filings. The latter were taken in aqua lumbricorum or aqua limacum composita, i.e. in watery extracts of the slime of worms and slugs.

His Oxford practice must have been unusually successful. Ward (38c) says that Willis had "rich peeces of plate presented to him as well as great ffees." Dewhurst (175) was able to deduce from the Poll Tax Returns of 1667 that Willis had then the highest income in Oxford (£ 300 per annum), and that he also paid the highest wages (£ 16 per annum, to the apothecary John Hemmings, his amanuensis). Willis invested his money in estates. (175)

Doctor Willis often rode far into the country to visit his patients. During the first years he had to share a horse with another physician. (175) On one of these trips he is said to have discovered the healing mineral qualities of the well at Astrop, in Northhamptonshire; Wood (1, Lower) tells us that the discovery was actually made by Lower, "the Doctor being then, as usually, asleep or in sleepy condition on Horseback." The two chemical doctors analyzed the water, found it equal to healing waters of high repute, and Willis began to recommend Astrop for cures.

Ward writes of Willis' scientific exploits:" [He] hath got a new way of opening ye Brains, as to cut them on all parts from what holds them and so to turn them upside down." In 1658 he made the following entry in his diary: (43a) "Dr. Willis and Dick Lower opened a dogg and they first let him blood in the jugulars to discover whether arterial and venal blood did differ in colour and constitution."

Willis' outward appearance was not very impressive, and he must have seemed rather drab among the *Vertuosi* who were mostly elegant men of pleasant manners and independent means. (33) Aubrey (6) remarks that he was of middle stature, had dark red hair, and stammered, and Wood (1) says: "he was a plain Man, a Man of no Carriage, little Discourse, Complaisance or Society. . . ."

In April 1657 Willis married Mary Fell. (1, 4a) Her father, Dr. Samuel Fell, former Dean of Christ Church College, had been ejected by the Rebels in 1648. According to his instructions, his family had declined to leave the deanery. Consequently the whole family, including Willis' future wife, had been carried out and deposited somewhere on the grass by soldiers. (23b) Mary's brother John was one of the three clergymen who had maintained the Anglican service in Willis' house throughout its suppression. By and by he became Canon and Dean of Christ Church College, vice-chancellor of the University, and Bishop of Oxford. As he was inclined to be rather strict in dealing with morality issues, he was not universally beloved in the University. and therefore became the subject of a well-known epigram: (22)

> I do not love thee, Doctor Fell,
> The reason why I cannot tell;
> But this alone I know full well,
> I do not love thee, Doctor Fell.

Before his marriage Willis had done much to secure the welfare of his family. Wood (quoted in (175)) writes: "When he came into business 'tis certain he maintained his brother and sisters. He paid several debts of his brother William, who dyed fellow of Trinity College, Oxford, as I find by his account and Mr. Benson his nephew, archdeacon of Hertford, who dyed a non-juror aged about 86 last year, told me. He had several sisters well married, and a puritanical brother one John Willis a good attorney, chapter clerk of Christ Church college who drew up all the leases &c of that college."

From 1658 to 1666 Mary Willis gave birth to four sons and four daughters. Three of the boys and one girl died soon. (4a) Only the eldest son, Thomas, born in 1658, survived his father. His son (Dr. Willis' grandson) was Browne Willis, the antiquary. (3)

In 1659 Willis' first book was published in London and The Hague: "Diatribae Duae" or "Two Medico-Philosophical Investigations . . . Concerning Fermentation and Fevers." The first part is a *natural philosophy* founded upon chymical and atomistic concepts. In the second part Willis' bedside observations of fevers are explained in terms of his natural philosophy. In the preface to "Of Fevers" he declares: "After I had not found in Books what might satisfy a mind desirous of Truth, I resolved with myself to reach into living and breathing examples: and therefore sitting oftentimes by the Sick, I was wont carefully to search out their cases, to weigh all the symptoms, and to put them, with exact Diaries of the Diseases, into writing; then diligently to meditate on these; and then began to adapt general Notions from particular events . . .". (G) Willis thus explains his book as a result of the inductive method as described by Bacon. In "Of Fermentation" he condemns the doctrine of the classical four elements as taught by the Aristotelians: ". . . 'tis almost the same thing, to say a house consists of wood and stone, as a Body of Four Elements." (De Ferm., 1, quoted after

(G) In "Of Fevers" he abolishes the doctrine of the four Galenic humors, which, as he states rightly, has been disproved by Harvey's discovery of the circulation of the blood. As an appendix to "Fermentation" and "Fevers" an "Epistolary Dissertation of the Urines" was published, addressed to Willis' friend Randolph Bathurst. Bathurst had "kept Abingdon Market" with Willis, and he had also been present at the resuscitation of Anne Green and at the Anglican services in Willis' house. (3)

In the year 1660 the time of the Puritans was up. With Charles II the Stuart Kings returned to power. A new body of Visitors went to work in Oxford. They ejected most of the University men installed by their predecessors, rehabilitated those who had been ejected before, and rewarded the loyal partisans of the King and the Church of England. Among these were the three divines who had upheld the Anglican tradition in the house of Willis. John Dolben and Richard Allestree were made Canons of Christ Church, and soon afterwards, Doctors of Divinity; Allestree later became Professor of Theology. John Fell, Willis' brother-in-law, was made Canon and Dean of Christ Church. (1, 3) One Doctor Joshua Crosse was removed from the Sedleian Chair of Natural Philosophy and found guilty of embezzlement. (47) In 1660 Willis was elected in his place. In the dedication of his first book (the "Diatribae Duae") Willis attributes his election as Sedleian Professor to the influence of Gilbert Sheldon, who became

Archbishop of Canterbury in 1663. (46) It is to him that Willis dedicated his later works.

According to the Laudian Code then in force, the Sedleian Professor of Natural Philosophy was ordered to read "... the Physica of Aristotle or [his] books about Heaven and Earth, or de Meteoris, or the small naturals by the same [Author], or the books about the Soul, also the books about Generation and Corruption, twice every week in a full Term, that is, on Wednesday and Saturday, at eight o'clock in the morning. [His] auditors shall be the Bachelors of Arts, the same that [are hearing] Astronomy." (11i) In sixteenth- and seventeenth-century Europe many progressive university teachers found themselves in the same constrained position. They often circumvented the regulations by duly explaining the teachings of Aristotle just to disprove them afterwards. (41d) Ramus and Gassendi had made use of the same method.

Most probably Willis, too, professed his own opinions in his official lectures. A passage in "The Natural History of Oxford-Shire" (48) by Robert Plot suggests that much. To judge from the dates of his matriculation and graduations, Plot must have heard Willis' Sedleian lectures. (1, 3) He writes: "In Natural Philosophy, the famous Dr. Willis . . . Sidleyan Professor . . . in this University, first taught us, that the Generations, Perfections, and Corruptions of Natural Bodies, whether Mineral, Vegetable, or Animal; and so likewise of Bodies Artificial, do depend upon Fermentations, raised from the different Proportions and Motions of Spirit, Sulphur, Salt, Water, and Earth, which he did constitute the ultimate sensible Principles of mixed Bodies." This sounds exactly like an explication, in the terms of Willis' "Of Fermentation," of a typically Aristotelian subject. However, Plot might as well have heard the same in private courses. As an extracurricular teacher of anatomy, medicine, and chemistry, Willis was quite prolific. (158, 166) Such lectures were rather more important for the development of scientific thought than the official ones, as they were not hampered by scholastic regulations.

The peculiar position of Willis as Professor of Natural Philosophy did not result from his being a physician; of his three predecessors two had been physicians. But Willis had shortly before declared himself an enemy of Aristotelian philosophy; at the time of his election as Professor, the Aristotelian influence in the University was rapidly growing due to the strongly traditional trend of the Restoration. In 1661 Edward Bagshaw was able to say: "He [Aristotle] has driven out all other philosophers, and rules supreme, especially in Christ Church. Here a temple and altar have been erected to the Stagirite as to a philosophical deity, to whom also festive days are consecrated and solemn pomp and annual panegyric dedicated. Here he walks and enjoys his praise as if he were the loci genius." (15)

Besides Lower, Hooke, Wren, and Plot, Gunther (38d) mentions John Mayow and John Locke as pupils of Willis. Locke, the physician and philosopher, attended Willis' courses, where he "filled half his note-book* with detailed Latin notes of his lectures on therapeutics." (158) These extra-curricular courses seem to have been held at Christ Church, whereas the Sedleian lectures took place in the School Building. (cf. 158) Locke's famous "Essay concerning human understanding" contains several concepts and ideas, that can be traced back to Willis. (cf. below p174ff.) Of John Mayow we know that he investigated the active principle of the air, later called oxygen, at the same time as Willis, Lower, Boyle and Hooke. (cf. below p144ff.) (43) Mayow knew at least some of Willis' theories, but it has been doubted that he actually was one of his pupils. (49) Willis' teachings seem to have been popular even among the clergy: Richard Allestree, Professor of Theology, ". . . went thro' a course of chymistry with Dr. Willis, which is the reason why so many physical and chymical allusions are found in his writings . . ." (166)

The movement of the *Vertuosi* as a whole was not endangered by the Restoration. The *Vertuosi* continued their propaganda for the New Science in spite of its inherent Puritan values, but they carefully avoided to demand any structural changes in the two universities. (16g) Nevertheless some of them were forced to leave Oxford, and others left because of the gradual decline of the progressive movement in the University. London again became the center of the New Science. In autumn 1660 the members of the

* Bodleian Library, MS Locke, f. 19, 1664-9, 412 pages (158).

"Invisible College" compiled a list of forty names. That was the first roll of the Royal Society of London for the Promotion of Natural Knowledge. The men listed in it were the leaders of the *Vertuosi,* who, ". . . if they should desire it, might be admitted before any others." (Birch, 50a) Among these forty candidates was Thomas Willis.

The gradual loss of their position in Oxford gave rise to a series of pamphlets by the *Vertuosi.* In 1661 the first book of young Joseph Glanvill was published: "The Vanity of Dogmatizing and Confident Opinion." Glanvill attacks the scholastic philosophy dominant in Oxford, upholding against it the new "natural philosophy." In a later treatise he revels in anticipations of a future improved by a technology founded upon the New Science. He would not hesitate to predict intercontinental air travel or flights to the moon. His anticipation of telegraphy is a good example for the optimism of the *Vertuosi:* ". . . to confer at the distance of the Indies by sympathetick contrivances may be as natural to future times as to us is a litterary correspondence." (3)

In 1664 Willis' great book about the anatomy of the brain and the nervous system, "Cerebri Anatome," was published in London. It was an immediate success, and pocket editions were printed in the same year in London and in Amsterdam. At that time already five editions of his first book were in existence. (63, 64) As Willis explicitly states in the preface, "Cerebri Anatome" was the result of teamwork with Lower, Christopher Wren, and Dr. Thomas Millington. Willis bestows special praise upon Lower's part in the work, describing his accurate way of dissecting with admiration. He declares that the illustrations of the first part were drawn by Wren, and the plans in the second part devised, verified and drawn by Lower. Willis tells us that scarcely a day passed without some "anatomical administration" (by Willis and Lower, cf. Cerebri Anatome, 1st ed.). It is well known, however, that the Oxford anatomists seldom received fresh corpses. (27, 173) We must therefore assume that Willis and his team were using chemical methods to preserve anatomical preparations. Such methods had been introduced a short time ago by Petty and Boyle. (21d, 27) For the *Vertuosi* teamwork in research was a matter of course: in order to facilitate it they founded their Royal Society. The idea behind this tendency was clearly that of a "commonwealth of philosophers," as outlined in many pamphlets of the Puritan Era. Questions of priority among the *Vertuosi* are therefore often insoluble, or at least even more illusory than they generally are. A good example of this may be found in the controversy between the professors Partington and Patterson about John Mayow. (43, 49)

Some medical historians of the nineteenth and the twentieth century professed that "Cerebri Anatome" was chiefly the work of Lower and his associates, and that Willis had not added to it much more than his name. (Foster and others, 11) This sort of criticism, a little suggestive of the well known efforts to disprove

Shakespeare's authorship of his own plays (cf. 174), has been refuted by Dow (55), Symonds (56), and Hierons/ Meyer. (108) They have proved that the former group relied on Wood (1, Willis), whose relevant sentence was taken nearly word for word from a book by Stubbe: "Whatsoever is anatomical in that Book, the Glory thereof belongs to the said R. Lower, whose indefatigable Industry at Oxon produced that elaborate Piece." They have further demonstrated that Stubbe, in a postscript to the same book, practically revokes his statement, ". . . lest the *Virtuosi* should censure me as partial to my old School-fellow, Dr. Lower, or swayed by any regard other than that of Truth." (6) They have shown that Wood held a grudge against the family of Willis, and that he was a friend of "Dick" Lower (as he calls him in his diary (4) , with whom he used to frequent Oxford taverns. (56) However, the most convincing proof of Willis' authenticity is in the importance of his other books: it should be pointed out that until now his work has not been reviewed as a whole.

In 1665 a treatise entitled "Examen Diatribae Thomae Willisii . . ." came out. It was written by Edmund O'Meara, a Bristol physician of Irish descent, who attacked Willis' book "Of Fevers" and the doctrines of Glisson and Harvey upon which some of Willis' theories had been founded. O'Meara's criticism was based on Galenic medicine and Aristotelian formalism. In the autumn of 1665 Lower replied in "Diatribae Thomae Willisii . . . Vindicatio . . ." (London).

Lower's defense of Willis has been called "the best testimony of their harmonious relations." (168) The language he uses against O'Meara is far from moderate. He simply calls him "a little frog from the swamps of Ireland." (58) On the Continent the controversy was followed with interest. In 1667 Gerbrand Schagen in Amsterdam edited a pocketbook containing O'Meara's "Examen," Lower's "Vindicatio," a treatise on hereditary diseases by O'Meara's father, and a reprint of Thomas Sydenham's first book "Methodus curandi febres," which had been published first in 1666. (58) The subject of Sydenham's book is closely related to that of Willis' "Of Fevers," and Sydenham has adopted some of the relevant ideas from Willis' book (see below p. 83ff.) . Lower's defense was answered in 1667 by one Conlo Cassinius in a pamphlet printed in Dublin, entitled "Willis badly defended, or: an Oxford physician found guilty of lying and ignorance." In his "De Corde" (London 1669) Lower explains Conlo Cassinius as a pseudonym for O'Meara, adding that he would not care to fight with him, as that would mean to descend onto a dunghill instead of an arena. (170)

Gerbrand Schagen may have had a good reason for publishing the texts of this controversy in 1667. The year 1666 was a turning point in medical history. It brought a decisive victory of the chemical doctors over their Galenic adversaries: on March 29th, 1666, of 102 doctors assembled in the Paris Faculty of Medicine, 92 voted in favor of listing "emetic wine" among the approved purgatives, thus giving free way to the therapeutic use of antimony, which had been disputed for a century. (60a, 156)

In England the dispute between the adherents of traditional and modern (16) medicine became more acute in 1665 when Marchamont Nedham's "Medela Medicinae" was published. This is really a manifesto of chemical medicine. Nedham invites the universities to follow the advice given by Willis in his first book and not to "lie down . . . under the shadow of a great name, and make an Idol of it. We should rather reject what runs to superstition, and not pin the Faith of mankind upon the sleeve of Hippocrates, because others have done so." Willis' analysis of matter is cited by Nedham "as an excellent example of Bacon's idea of raising a philosophy upon sensible experiments." (Jones, 16i) Like Willis' "Of Fevers," which contains most of the essential ideas of these later pamphlets, Nedham's treatise led to a series of attacks and counterattacks. In this conflict the chymists were the protagonists on the side of modern medicine. They considered themselves the champions of experimental science, identifying the interpretation of nature in crude chemical terms with the inductive method. They even demanded the establishment of a Royal Chemical Society, referring to Willis and Goddard as their authorities. (16)

In this decade the war between "ancients and moderns" was waged more vehemently in medicine than in the other fields of knowledge. (16i) In Oxford the influence of the ancients increased, and the University lost its importance in the scientific movement. In London, where the New Science had gained a secure foothold by the founding of the Royal Society, many physicians had died in the Great Plague of 1665, and still more had fled from the city. Such were the circumstances when Willis was called to London by the Archbishop of Canterbury, Gilbert Sheldon, who had his residence there. (1, 3)

Willis did not resign from his Oxford chair when he moved to London. He kept the office of Sedleian Professor until his death. (10b) In his absence the Sedleian lectures were held by a deputy, as was usual in such cases; the extracurricular courses were at first continued by Lower. (175) Wood (4b) relates that Cosimo de' Medici, while visiting Oxford in May 1669, heard a lecture held in the School of Natural Philosophy by Willis' deputy George Hooper. Afterwards a disputation was enacted by two bachelors of arts: they affirmed that the "Medicean Stars be the moons of Jupiter," and they duly denied the feasibility of empty space. George Hooper was a master of arts of Christ Church College who excelled in classical languages and mathematics. (3) He was to become a bishop. The implications of the concept of Jovian moons had been reluctantly accepted by the *ancients,* but the notion of empty space was a major stumbling block to them. In Willis' "Of Fermentation" empty space is not overtly mentioned, but it is inherent in its theories.

A passage from Henry Stubbe gives further indication to the point that the *ancients* must have been relieved by the departure of Thomas Willis. In a pamphlet directed against Bacon and the *Vertuosi* he writes: (51) " 'Tis true there is a Professor of Natural Philosophy in Oxford . . . and the reason is because that the interest of our Monarchy is an Interest of Religion, and the support of the Religion established by Law is complicated with, and depends upon, those Studies: 'Tis no less than impossible for any man to understand or manage the controversies with the Papists . . . without a deep knowledge of those Sciences . . ."—here follows an enumeration of Aristotelian terms that have to be understood in order to settle the question of transubstantiation—"For if we change our Notions in Natural Philosophy, we then differ in the principles of discourse; and where men differ therein 'tis impossible for them to proceed. . . . By the change agitated, and now pursued, we make our selves incapable of convincing a papist: and considering the prejudices of long Education, and the authority of the Catholic Church, we must render our selves in their judgment as Perfect Fooles, and not to be able to proceed, is in their case all one to be baffled."

After Willis' death in 1675 Sir Thomas Millington became Professor of Natural Philosophy. He had helped to prepare "Cerebri Anatome" with Willis' research team. He was one of the first *Vertuosi*, is known for his early theory of the sexual functions of plants, and was appreciated as a physician by Sydenham. His lectures were mostly held by a deputy. (3)

In 1666, as Wood (1) writes, Willis took "a tenement" in St. Martin's Lane in London. It seems that he definitely settled there at a later date, as there is evidence that travellers made a detour to Oxford to ask for his advice as late as May 1667. (166) He even took long leases in 1666 for two houses at a site that was preferred for medical practice: the Angel, and Boster Hall, in High Street, near the place where the stage coaches going to Bath used to stop. (Dewhurst, 175) During his last years in Oxford Willis had to pay high taxes, and Dewhurst (175) thinks that he tried to dodge them. Tax problems might have been one of the motives for his final departure from Oxford.

Willis' fame followed him to London, and ". . . in very short time after he became so noted, and so infinitely resorted to, for his practice, that never any physician before went beyond him, or got more Money yearly than he." (1) His success with the general public is all the more remarkable because he failed to establish good relations at Court. He had made a careless remark to a colleague about the health of Charles II's Queen, and "being called to consult for one of [the Duke of York's] sons, gave his opinion in those words, mala stamina vitae, which gave such offence, that he was never called for afterwards." (Bishop Burnet, 1665; (52, 54) Willis' statement was a slightly veiled diagnosis of hereditary or congenital disease, the effects of, as Burnet puts it, "the dregs of a tainted original." This was confirmed afterwards by the remarkably bad health of the Duke's family. (Burnet, ibid.) Charles II seems to have had an ill concealed aversion against Willis. He is reputed to have said that Willis rid him of more of his subjects than any enemy army. (53) But the teachings of Willis were followed at Court: we know that a young Court physician, Thomas Sherley, adopted Willis' doctrine of the fevers. (62)

Willis was admitted to the Royal Society on October 24th, 1667. (50b) From then on his name sometimes appears in its proceedings. In November 1667 Willis presented his new book about convulsive diseases; Boyle and Willis were charged to examine the chemical properties of an artificial Spa-water, which Willis found of no value. (50c) In December Dr. King* performed a transfusion of sheep's blood into one Mr. Arthur Coga, who was not greatly harmed by the procedure. In the subsequent discussion somebody proposed to try the new therapy on suitable patients in London hospitals, and Dr. Willis suggested, that this experiment might be proper to make use of upon "rotten sheep." (50d) Willis appeared among the persons who were thought both willing and able to contribute to the building of the Society's new college. On June 30th,

* Sir Edmund King, a surgeon in Lóndon, graduated doctor of medicine by decree of the Archbishop of Canterbury, Gilbert Sheldon. He is mentioned as a friend and assistant in the prefaces to "De Anima Brutorum" and "Pharmaceutice Rationalis." His main field of research was the anatomy of blood vessels. In the "Philosophical Transactions" of the Royal Society he published: in 1666 a tract about the structure of the parenchymatous organs, in 1667 a description of a blood transfusion from calf to sheep, and in 1669 an article about the glands, which he said to consist merely of tubes and vessels. He was acquainted with Petty, Nedham, and Boyle. His house was noted for a great collection of curiosities, mainly dried anatomical preparations (3).

1671, a letter from De le Boe Sylvius was read, who had sent some of his books to the Society; Willis was presented with a copy of his "Praxeos Medicae Idea Nova." (50e) From time to time Dr. King gave an account of Willis' researches, in which he took part. On November 25th, 1675, it was agreed upon "That it be recommended to the care of Dr. King, to solicit the executors of the late Dr. Willis for the payment of his arrears to the Society, amounting to twenty pounds and eleven shillings, as appeared from the treasurer's book." (50f)

In 1667 Willis' first book about nervous diseases was published: "Specimen of the pathology of the brain and the nervous system" contains a discussion of scurvy and the convulsive diseases, that is, epilepsy, hysteria, hypochondria, and other diseases accompanied or characterised by spasms. Willis refuted the ancient explanation of hysteria as a disease of the womb, and he also refuted a theory advanced by Harvey's friend, Nathanael Highmore, who believed the chest to be the seat of the disease. Highmore replied to that rather harshly in "De Hysterica et Hypochondriaca Passione," published in 1670. In 1671 Willis defended his opinion in a tract entitled "Affectionum Hystericae et Hypochondriacae . . . Pathologia vindicata . . .," to which he appended two short essays, one about "the accension of the blood" containing a theory of animal metabolism based on combustion, the other about the mechanics of muscular movement.

In the autumn of 1670 Willis' wife Mary died, probably from tuberculosis. (Snow Miller, 54) As Snow Miller writes, his son Thomas had already been to Montpellier to get himself cured from the same disease. Nevertheless, in 1672 Willis published his next book, which he had written, as he says in the preface, to alleviate his sorrow after the loss of his dear wife. The book "Of the Soul of Brutes" had been planned as early as 1664; in a postscript to "Cerebri Anatome" of 1664, the project of a Willisian "Psychologia" is announced as a logical and necessary consequence. Together with "Specimen of the pathology of the brain . . ." of 1667 and the "Defence of the Pathology . . . of the Hysterical and Hypochondriacal Affection . . ." of 1670, the book represents the first complete text of psychiatry. Like "Cerebri Anatome," "Of the Soul of Brutes" is founded upon the results of a research team; this time Willis had Drs. King and Master as his assistants. (preface)

In 1672 Willis married a widow, Elizabeth Calley, who survived him for many years. (3) It is said that in his late years he cared much for the poor and gave all his Sunday fees for their relief. (5, 54) His grandson, Browne Willis, writes (5) that at his death the sum of £ 237 was found in a box labeled "for the poor," out of a total sum of £ 1528. In the church of St. Martin's-in-the-fields near his house, Willis had an evening service read, at his expense, which was continued after his death. (54)

Wood (1) speaks of "a great deal of drudgery, that he did undergo in his Faculty, (mostly for Lucre sake) which did much shorten his Life. . . ." By "Faculty" Wood most probably means the Royal College of Physicians, which at that time, according to Jones (16), was a stronghold of Galenism. Willis had been elected honorary fellow of the College in 1664, and it is very likely that he had to suffer from the repercussions of the struggle of the chemical doctors against the Galenists that became acute in 1666. (cf. 16)

In 1674 the first part of Willis' "Pharmaceutice Rationalis" came out. It contains a systematic listing of medicaments by the localization of their effects, often based on sound anatomical and physiological knowledge. The second part, published posthumously at the end of 1675, consists mainly of exemplary descriptions of diseases together with their morbid (pathologic) anatomy.

In November 1675 Willis contracted a bad cough that soon developed into a "Pleurisy and Peripneumonia." He died of it on November 11th, 1675, having retained his consciousness to the last. (54)

"He left behind him the Character of an Orthodox, Pious, and Charitable Physician," says Wood (1), who was not without prejudice against him, and "The truth is, tho' he was a plain Man, a Man of no Carriage, little Discourse, Complaisance or Society, yet for his deep Insight, happy Researches in natural and experimental Philosophy, Anatomy and Chymistry, for his wonderful Success and Repute in his practice, the natural smoothness, pure elegancy, delightful, unaffected neatness of Lat. Stile, none scarce hath equall'd, much less out-done him, how great soever. When at any time he is mention'd by Authors (as he is very often) it is done in Words expressing their highest Esteem of his great Worth and Excellency, and placed still, as first in Rank, among Physicians."

At the time of his death all his earlier works had reached several editions in England and on the Continent. (40, 63, 64) The second part of "Pharmaceutice Rationalis" was in the press. (24) In the preface to it Willis had written: (F) "If these slight attempts should animate others the better to cultivate these studies, I shall not at all regret my work, notwithstanding the abuse heaped on me by the envious and the malevolent. When I shall be well conscious that I have not spent my feeble gifts (as a Talent entrusted to me by God Almighty) in vain through idleness, nor buried them in the Earth, and that they may be rendered with interest beyond the capital, I shall like it well, indeed, I shall truly rejoice and triumph."

II. WILLIS' WORKS

TWO INVESTIGATIONS

Willis' first book came out in 1659 in London and The Hague. (3, 88) It was written in Latin and entitled "Diatribae Duae Medico-Philosophicae . . ."*, that is: Two Medical-Philosophical Investigations, the First of Fermentation, or the Internal Motion of Particles in all kinds of Bodies, the Second of the Fevers, or the Motion of said [Particles] in the blood of Animals: to which is appended an Epistolary Dissertation on the Urines.

Further Latin editions appeared in London in 1660, 1662, 1677, in Amsterdam in 1663 and 1669, in Geneva in 1676 and 1694 (these last two editions were parts of "Opera Omnia" published separately). A Dutch version came out in Middelburgh (Zeeland) in 1676 as "Nieuwe . . . verhandeling . . . van de fermentatie. . . ."

* Thomae Willis Diatribae Duae Medico-Philosophicae / Prior agit de Fermentatione, sive de Motu Intestino Particularum in quovis Corpore; Altera de Febribus, sive de Motu earundem in sanguine Animalium: His accessit Dissertatio Epistolica de Urinis.

"Of the Urines" was reprinted in Latin in an augmented edition of the "Libri de Urinis" by Johannes Actuarius. (Utrecht 1670) The same book was published in French in Paris, 1683. The "Investigations" have been reprinted in the Latin editions of Willis' complete works (Lyons 1676, Amsterdam 1682, Venice 1720) and in the English translation, entitled "Dr. Willis's Practice of Physick." (London 1684)

OF FERMENTATION

This is the only work by Willis that contains mainly chemical theories. The very first sentence shows the author's disdain for Aristotelian philosophy. "There is nothing more rarely to be met with in the Vulgar Philosophy," he writes, "where Natural things are unfolded, with the vain figments of Forms and Qualities, than the word Fermentation: but among the more sound (especially of later years) who respect the Matter and Motion chiefly in Bodies, nothing is almost more usual." (AA, 1, p. 1, quoted from G)

Fermentation occurs in bread and in beverages. Willis applies the term to similar phenomena in other kinds of matter. Fermentation is, to him, "whatsoever Effervency or Turgency, that is raised up in a Natural Body, by particles of that Body variously agitated." (AA, 1, p. 1, quoted from G) Bodies of very dissimilar constitution may be subject to fermentation, but only if they contain heterogeneous particles. Most of the simpler preparations of the Chymists are very stable. Compound liquors, such as juices of plants, or the blood of animals, begin to ferment after a short time, changing in different ways. A distillate from herbs, for instance, will stay undisturbed for a long time when kept alone in a vial. If it is mixed with sugar or syrup, it will shortly grow sour and perish.

In order to explain the fermentation of bodies correctly we have to answer the following question: What are the substances, or particles, of which mixed bodies consist, and from which depend most natural movements? There are three answers of importance. The Aristotelians ascribe everything to Water, Fire, Air, and Earth. The doctrine of Democritus and Epicurus, recently renewed, refers all effects in nature to atoms of different shapes. But the doctrine of the Chymists, "making an analysis by fire and dissolving any bodies into particles of spirit, sulphur, salt, water, and earth, affirms by the best reasons that the former consist of the latter." (AA, 1, p. 2)

The Aristotelian doctrine has helped a little towards an explanation of the phenomena of nature, but it is all too content with the outward appearance of things. The Epicurean theory is worthy of praise, as it solves some intricate scientific questions in a mechanical way without seeking refuge in hidden qualities,* or sympathy,** or other asylums of ignorance. But it does

* One of the main concepts of Aristotelian natural philosophy.
** A term denoting hidden connections of magic quality: e.g. between

rather suppose than demonstrate, teaching more the shape than the identity of the elements, and introducing opinions that go far astray from the sensible and do not fit in with natural phenomena when examined closely. Willis therefore consents to the doctrine of the Chymists. "However, should someone reply that the atomist, and our chymical principles do wholly belong together . . . I will not much battle against him; let him but demonstrate the reality of those concepts. Night-blind and dullwitted, I leave the more accurate questions to those of sharper view (lynceis*) ; I am content to know what the external senses provide to the reasoning mind; to wit, I readily profess that I do not want to fabricate or to dream of a philosophy." (AA, 1, p. 2)

THE FIVE PRINCIPLES

"By the name of [chymical] principles I do not mean the simplest uncombined entities, but only such substances into which physical things are resolved as into their last sensible parts. Bodies come into being, and grow, by their combination and internal movement: by

the excrements and the defecator (van Helmont) , or between a weapon and the wound it has made. The concept was very common in sixteenth and seventeenth century medicine until the breakthrough of experimental science; it goes back to the Stoics and Plotinus (67) .

* "Lynceis" refers to the Accademia dei lincei, the first of the many learned societies founded in the seventeenth century. The *Vertuosi* were inspired, directly and indirectly, by the Italians, as their Italian name shows. As appears from the context, Willis meant the followers of Gassendi.

their mutual departure the bodies are altered and corrupted. In the meantime the particles that are being gathered together in the subjects, or falling apart from them, appear in the form of spirit, sulphur, salt, or one of the other [principles"]. (AA, 1, p. 2)

The spirits are "a most subtle and ethereal Substance, and particles of a more divine hue, which the father of nature created in this sublunar world as instruments of life and soul, movement and sense of all things. . . ." (AA, 2, p. 3) They determine the shape of things. From their motion arise the animation of bodies, the growth of plants, the ripening of fruits and liquors. Since they are highly volatile, they may be found chiefly in compounds together with coarser particles, or, uncombined, in the vessels and intestines of animals. In crude, unripe bodies they are so strongly bound to the coarser particles that they cannot easily be separated from them and therefore stay inactive. If they are less strongly bound, they impart their motion to the coarser particles, so that the crude is digested, the coarse refined. They make the bodics perfect and stable: if they are completely freed, they depart, and the bodies perish.

Sulphur is a little coarser and denser than the spirits.* But it is more ferocious and unbridled than those, and if it is not retained in a compound with other principles, it departs from the body, destroying it

* Willis writes "spirit" as well as "spirits," "salt" and "salts," with the notion of different spirits and salts; of water, earth and sulphur he writes only in the singular.

by its too impetuous outbreak. Sulphur is a most mobile principle, second in that respect only to the spirits. In chemical analysis, i.e. distillation, it ascends immediately after the spirits. The spirits are bound to the other principles by sulphur. Sulphur is the base of colors, odors, and heat. Its substance is never encountered in a pure state, since any separation from the other principles would volatilize it. Sulphur may be irrevocably bound to salt and earth, as in metals and minerals, or it may be dissolved in water, or in spirit. Sulphur may be in one of three different stages of solution: it may be suppressed by salt, earth, or water, so that the body containing it will be cold and damp, or it may be exalted above the other principles, together with spirit, engendering strength, maturity, and heat; it may be leaving the mixture, so that the body comes apart.

If sulphur departs from a mixture without great disturbance, accompanied by spirit and water, the dried body will dissolve into dust. If the spirits leave a mass that has been turgid with much sulphur, the sulphurous particles become much agitated and effervescent, and putrefaction occurs; sometimes, as in moist hay, combustion may result. If the sulphurous particles leave the mixture with continued violence, they break out in flames, and the mixture is destroyed.

Salt is a little more stable than spirit and sulphur, and less inclined to be volatilized. It gives to things solidity, duration, and weight, retarding their dissolution, promoting congelation and coagulation, and resisting putrefaction, corruption and combustion, because it retains sulphur and spirit in the bodies. Not only the duration of the individual, but also the propagation of the species depends mostly upon the principle of salt: the growth of minerals, the fertility of the earth, the growth of plants, and, above all, the procreation of animals, arise from saline seed. Salt in a fused state reassembles the idle or highly dispersed particles of spirit and sulphur, inciting them to ordered movement, and thus helping to produce the initial groundwork of things.

Salt may exist in a fixed state in compounds with earth and sulphur. In watery solutions its particles are mixed with others, mostly spirit and sulphur, and they unfold, expand, and ferment together with them. Again, Willis describes three different states: fusion, volatilization, and flux (fluor).

In fusion the particles dissolve completely and expand through the whole mixture, which consequently turns unpleasant and undigested, and disagreeable, harsh, and bitter to the taste. In volatilization these particles unfold their force together with the particles of spirit and sulphur, inciting the substance into maturation. In this state the salts rise in the alembic in the same way as the spirits. In flux the saline particles are freed of their bonds to earth, sulphur, or spirit; most of the particles of spirit and sulphur depart, and salt dominates the mixture, imparting to it a sour taste, as in sour milk, spoiled victuals, and stale blood. For the same reason salts turn sour when they have been driven out of their compounds with earth by violent distillation. If the resultant sour liquid is poured on the remaining compounds, the salty taste returns.

Spirit, sulphur, and salt are the active principles. Water and earth are merely inert principles that fill the space between the other particles. Water is the most suitable vehicle for the mutual reactions of the active principles; these reactions are very much dependent on the proportion between water and dissolved matter. In distillation earth practically never mounts in the alembic: it stays below as a residue, a "caput mortuum," and is therefore called "terra damnata," Condemned Earth. (AA, 2)

FERMENTATION IN NATURAL AND ARTIFICIAL BODIES

Fermentation is the internal motion of the particles or principles of any body. It brings the bodies to perfection, or changes them into others. It is found in minerals, plants, animals, and in artificial products and experiments.

It is by fermentative principles that minerals are built up in the bowels of the earth. Springs, meteoric phenomena, and atmospheric changes also arise from them, which may be verified in Gassendi's writings. Fermentation in plants is much more obvious, and its functions are important for all stages of life. It is so certain that the bodies of animals consist of said particles that there is no need to prove it (ut probatione non indigeat, (AA, 5, p. 11)). Life is engendered by a fermentation in the heart; fever arises from another fermentation in the blood; and the chylus, or nutrient humor, is made by a fermentation in the intestines. Some (for instance: van Helmont and Nathanael Highmore) say that a ferment is conveyed to the stomach from the spleen: but no pathway is found between spleen and stomach, and it might rather be possible that this ferment is produced in the stomach by residues of food that cling to its walls, in the same way as sourdough, which develops into useful ferment after having been subjected to fermentation. The animal spirit in the brain is also produced by fermentation. The fermentative particles from the sexual parts replenish the blood in the whole body as with a living ferment (velut vivido fermento (AA, 5, p. 13)). The spleen also animates the entire blood by its fermentation.

Yellow bile is formed into a ferment in the liver: it causes an effervescence in the nutrient pap in the intestines by which the elementary constituents of the pap can be worked up into smaller particles (minutius subigantur (AA, 5, p. 14)). Thus the purer part of the pap can be squeezed into the lacteals as a nutrient humor.

"We are not only born and nourished by the means of Ferments; but we also Dye: Every Disease (excites) its Tragedies by the strength of some Ferment."* (AA, 5, p. 14, quoted from G) Fever is caused by an effervescence of sulphur and spirit in the circulating blood. If the salt in the blood gets into a flux, the blood turns sour, bitter, or harsh, and scurvy or chronic diseases result.

We have to make use of fermentation for curing diseases. The physician's work is nearly the same as that of a vintner (fere idem est ac Oenopolae officium (AA, 5, p. 14)). Like wine, blood and the humors have to be kept in well-tuned fermentation. Excessive heat of the blood is subdued by bleeding and damping remedies, alien matter is removed by purgatives, vomitives, and sudorifics, weak blood is strengthened by cardiacs and digestives and, chiefly, iron preparations (chalybeata).

The phenomena of fermentation in artificial bodies are abundant. If these bodies are in the right state of unequal combination, loose bondage of particles, and moderate maturity, they can be brought into fermentation by an absolute or relative ferment. An absolute ferment is a body in which all active particles are strongly moving, by their movement carrying along all kinds of particles. Yeast, beaten eggs, and similar things are absolute ferments. A relative ferment, for the most part, consists of certain particles which cause an effervescence when they encounter particles of a certain other kind. In this way saline particles in the state of

* Nec tantum ratione fermentorum nascimur aut nutrimur: sed et morimur: quilibet morbus virtute fermenti cujusdam suas excitat tragedias. "Ferment" as used by Willis connotes "ferment" as well as "enzyme" (cf. 60, 85, 86, 87).

flux react with particles of other kinds, as in the well-known reaction of vinegar-like fluids with coral or iron filings.

Fermentation in wine, beer, and vinegar is studied thoroughly by Willis, as these are the best known examples of fermentation. It is possible that Willis still found opportunities to study viniculture in England (cf. Jullien, (68)); anyway, he could find vintners in Oxford (171) who probably did not know less about the production of wine than today's wine merchants. Putrefaction and dissolution in solvents are further kinds of fermentation. The vinegar-eels and the worms found on decaying bodies both originate from the escaping active principles. Dissolution in water consists in the reception of the particles to be dissolved in the pores and passages between the particles of water. Fire is a very potent dissolving agent, second only to water. Fire is nothing but the violent evasion of the sulphurous particles from a body.

Willis describes sulphur as a blackish, oily, sticky substance of bad smell, that comes out in distillation after the spirits and before the salts. We may assume from his description that *sulphur* must have consisted mainly of carbohydrates. His explanation of fire from "Of Fermentation," together with the "nitre" theory of 1670, was at least not worse than the phlogiston theories of the eighteenth century.

The most important effects of fire, heat and light, arise from emanations and effluvia issuing from the burning body. Heat without light, or light without perceptible heat may also occur. Heat is conveyed directly or indirectly by the sulphurous particles that penetrate all obstacles and cause internal motion in the subject. Light appears to be a flame subtly dispersed, burning in great dimensions. The particles proceed from the source of light very fast in a straight line, the foremost being pushed ahead by those behind them. These rays are dispersed in an orb (in orbem). Whenever they fall upon a solid body they are either refracted and immersed or reflected. As the surfaces of the bodies are irregularly shaped, the rays are irregularly refracted and twisted: thus colors and shapes are produced out of the light which is the same for all bodies, although shapes and colors do not really exist. The effigy of the subject is represented near the retina by the fluid in the eye that acts as a lens. By this image a motion is impressed into the filaments of the optic nerve, and by this motion the act of vision is accomplished in the brain (ac dein à motu, quem haec imago fibrillis nervi optici imprimit, visionis actus in cerebro perficitur.) (AA, 10, p. 34)

Fermentation is also found in precipitations, for example in the production of cheese and butter. The separation of the serous part from the remainder of the blood which takes place in the kidneys is a fermentative precipitation, promoted by something like rennet. That is why diuretics are of the same kind as the substances that curdle milk. The precipitations produced by the Chymists also result from fermentation. Lastly, coagulation and congelation are fermentative processes.

VERDICTS OF MEDICAL HISTORY

In medical history Willis is unanimously placed among the Iatrochemists, a school or group of physicians that attempted to solve medical problems by methods, analogies, and remedies based on early chemistry. This movement has not always been reliably described. In Diderot's famous Encyclopedia, d'Aumont writes about a school of Iatrochemistry allegedly founded by van Helmont (Article: Fermentation, économie animale (69)). The same has been stated by F. H. Garrison in his history of medicine. (70) J. Pagel (71), Haeser, and Isensee (72) mention De le Boë Sylvius as the founder of the school. Meyer-Steinegg/Sudhoff (73) concede that Iatrochemistry existed before Sylvius, maintaining that Sylvius was the first to found a school. More light has been shed on these relations by Partington's "History of Chemistry" (60) where Paracelsus, the inventor of the term, is quoted as follows: "I am an Iatrochemist: since I know both medicine and chemistry."* (60e) Another passage from Partington shows that Johann Hartmann (1568-1631), Europe's first professor of chemistry, called himself "Chymiatriae professor" as early as 1609. (60d) Partington describes more than twenty early contemporaries of van Helmont under the heading "Iatrochemists following Paracelsus." (60f)

"Of Fermentation" and "Of Fevers" depend much

* Iatrochemista sum: vtrumque enim scio et Medicinam et Chemiã.

more upon chemical concepts than Willis' other works. They certainly belong to the Iatrochemical movement, and this is generally acknowledged in medical history, but most authors disagree upon the main influences behind Willis' Iatrochemical views. Leibbrand/Wettley state that "Of Fermentation" is written in Sylvius' way of thinking. (74a) Baas (75) writes of a "theory of his own, having but few points in common with that of Sylvius . . . whose Fermentation he accepts." Sprengel (76a) says: "His system is . . . quite as different from the theories of his contemporaries as it comes near to that of Paracelsus." C. A. Wunderlich (77) calls Willis the most important and independent among all the followers of the Sylvian doctrine who "essentially promoted the iatrochemical hypotheses while modifying and limiting them." Kopp (66a) writes about "Willis, who still combined the belief in the Paracelsian elements with his conviction of the rightness of the Sylvius System." Meyer-Steinegg/Sudhoff (73) come to the following conclusion: ". . . to designate this man as a pupil of Sylvius would be wrong . . . still, in Willis' further development Sylvius' influence cannot be ignored." Disagreements like these are characteristic of the historical evaluation of Willis and his works. They even appear within Diderot's Encyclopedia: Venel, a chemist, puts Willis' definition at the head of his article "Fermentation, chymie," thus acknowledging it as classic, whereas the physician d'Aumont writes in his article "Fermentation, économie animale" that the Iatrochemical school of van Helmont and

Sylvius is disproved and has become obsolete;* he denounces Willis as a source of needless confusion. (69)

In an evaluation of Willis' book on fermentation the early history of the concept ought to be considered, since the word and the idea are encountered again and again in the writings of Paracelsus and other early chymists and Iatrochemists. Many ideas from these writings reappear in Willis' book. Paracelsus explained putrefaction as a kind of fermentation (60g) and ascribed the "growth of minerals" to a struggle between salt and sulphur in the earth. (60h) Basil Valentine described a number of processes of which fermentation consists. (60i) In 1606 Andreas Libavius explained fermentation as a motion caused by a ferment in a moveable subject (60k), and in 1633 Angelus Sala called it an internal motion of the particles of bodies. (60 1) In 1619 Daniel Sennert said that all fermentations, separations, and concoctions, whether natural or artificial, depend only on the division of bodies into their smallest particles and the reunion of these particles. (60m) Francis Bacon wrote that yeast, leaven, curd, and certain poisons set up a successive and continued motion in dough, beer, cheese, or the human body. (60n) Even Jean Fernel had become aware of this basic idea of early biochemistry: he compared sanguification, the production of blood in the liver, to a fermentation. (81) And Gassendi referred the growth of rock crystal to an

* D'Aumont says that van Helmont and Sylvius founded the Iatrochemical school chiefly upon the assumption of an acid ferment in the stomach. According to d'Aumont gastric acid is an accidental artifact and is never found under normal conditions.

inner seed acting as a ferment. (60t) Fermentation "was in earlier times the most investigated chemical phenomenon in the realm of the organic . . ." (Hjelt, Hist. of Organic Chemistry (78)).

It is striking how often van Helmont speaks of ferment, and how seldom he uses the term fermentation. (60o, 79, 80) Besides the theory of digestive ferments no rationalist explanation of fermentation, or of the way his ferments work, can be found in his writings. His ferments do not appear, as Willis' do, as forms of mutual intercourse of elementary particles. A ferment, in van Helmont's view, is "a formal, created entity that has been founded neither as a substance nor as an accidens, but as a neuter, from the world's beginning, in the places of its Monarchy . . . so that it prepares, excites, and precedes the seeds (semina)." The ferments are "a gift, and roots, confirmed by the creator, the Lord . . ., which are to produce their own seeds out of water." (79a) A ferment is ". . . an odour, or a quality, that disposes a mass towards alteration or corruption . . ." (qualitas dispositiva ad alteritatem, etc., (79b)).

The conviction of van Helmont that "no transmutation happens in things . . . except through the action of the ferment . . ." is quite suggestive of Willis' theory that we come into existence, are nourished, and die by the property of some ferment: but this is hardly sufficient proof to explain Willis' whole chemical system as descending from that of van Helmont. It is possible that Willis' idea of the fermentative causes of all diseases goes back to van Helmont: but here we have to take into account the predominant difference between the terms of the two authors. Willis knew the writings of van Helmont; in "Of Fermentation" he writes about him, but in a depreciative way, accusing him of bragging of a universal solvent, which Willis believes to be quite as disappointing as the philosopher's stone. (Of Ferm., 9) Only once Willis' language is suggestive of the style of the Flemish mystic: "The spirits are . . . particles of a divine hue, which the father of nature did create in this sublunar world as instruments of life and soul, of motion and sense of all things . . ." (Of Ferm., 2) Although his attitude resembles that of van Helmont, there is a great difference in meaning. The "gift, and roots" of van Helmont clearly belong to a world full of magic, whereas the "instruments" of Willis which can be shown by distillation are parts of an environment that can be described in technical terms. Moreover, there is far more similarity between that statement of Willis and the terms of "the first completely developed system of corpuscular philosophy," that of Sebastian Basso (Lasswitz, 20), than between the description of the spirits in Willis and that of the ferments in van Helmont. Basso (20) is probably the source of Willis' concept of the spirits: in 1621 he already distinguished between the same five elementary principles as did Willis; he partly identified spirit with the ether of the Stoics, saying that spirit was used by God to bring about the motion of all things; spirit, as Basso wrote, is the best and noblest part of all things; it holds the other atoms together; it is the prime and common means by which Basso's pantheistic God acts. This theory has been taken up again by Isaac Newton. (Lasswitz, 20)

De le Boë Sylvius published his first iatrochemical work, the "Disputations," in 1663. (63, 83) An indirect influence upon Willis' earlier works cannot be excluded by this fact alone; but Sylvius' definition of fermentation differs clearly from that of Willis. Sylvius explains fermentation as a solution of salt through water, salt being the link between the other particles. "Fermentation," as Sylvius says, originally appears in fruit juices, beer, and bread, but it also exists in digestion in the mouth and stomach. If a stench arises from fermentation, it is called putrefaction. Fermentation has to be distinguished from the effervescence caused by acid-alkali-reactions, which is something far different. (82a)

The prevailing uncertainty in historical evaluation of Iatrochemistry becomes obvious in the divergence of opinions about Willis' five chymical principles. Willis himself writes: ". . . we have resolved to give our vote to the third sentence, *which is that of the Chymists,* and to insist chiefly upon this in the following tract: for they state that all bodies consist of spirit, sulphur, salt, water, and earth . . ."*. In spite of this clear statement, "almost everybody writing about it"

* . . . tertiae sententiae, quae chymicorum est, placuit calculum nostrum apponere, atque huic in sequenti tractatu praecipue insistere: statuentes nimirum corpora quaevis e Spiritu, Sulphure, Sale, Aqua, et Terra constare . . . (Of Ferm., 1) . Italics added.

(Partington, 60p) "copied Venel's remark in the encyclopédie." (69, Art.: Chymie) Venel says there that Willis was the first to add water and earth to the three Paracelsian principles. But Willis, although he declared that his five elements were not his own invention, did not name his sources. According to Partington (60p), Willis probably accepted the corpuscular theory of five principles from Sebastian Basso, a Pantheist who identified God with nature. (Lasswitz, 20) As we have shown above (61f.), Willis and Basso have some important ideas in common; and Basso's pantheism would certainly be a good reason for Willis not to cite him by name. But it is also possible that Willis refers to the mostly technical textbooks of the early chymists: in England chemistry had been a rather menial art before it was given the status of a nearly scientific occupation by the *Vertuosi:* there would be no reason to mention names that commanded no special attention. (cf. 19, 20, 33, 34, 60) Willis mentions Gassendi and his followers, but not as sources of his corpuscular ideas: again, Basso's "first complete corpuscular philosophy" or the early technical manuals are likely to be behind them. (cf. Lasswitz and Hoykaas, (20) These manuals were so widely known at the time that most authors did not see any need to cite them, since they were the common foundations of chemistry. (20, 45, 89) Quite like Willis, Francis Glisson did not care to name the sources of his chymical theory. Not later than 1659*

* In: Anatomia Hepatis, Amsterdam 1659. The five principles appear also in "De Rachitide," of which no early edition was accessible.

Glisson had accepted the same doctrine of five corpuscular principles, declaring that ". . . I believe that the opinion of the Chymists is the most true." Like Willis, Glisson was one of the first *Vertuosi.* He belonged to the London group when Willis was a *Vertuoso* in Oxford. Both groups were closely connected. It is highly probable that subjects of such importance as the doctrine of five corpuscular principles were discussed simultaneously and extensively in both groups.

EVALUATION

Willis declares to be "content to know only what the external senses provide to the mind," and "not willing to fabricate a philosophy." He thus commits himself to a pragmatical attitude as demanded by the *Vertuosi* and, before, by Francis Bacon. Today one might call it scientific objectivity. But in "Of Fermentation" Willis does not succeed in this endeavor. It was hardly possible in his age to keep away from unfounded theories and beliefs: neither the *Vertuosi,* nor Bacon himself, nor Sydenham, whose demands were even more exclusive, could avoid makeshift explanations, undisciplined thinking, and the law of least resistance. Willis' doctrine of five principles is mostly hypothetical, though perhaps more founded upon experimental data than comparable theories of the time. The spirits as particles of a divine hue, the minerals growing in the earth, procreation due to salt, and similar notions of Willis are certainly not results of "what the external senses provide to the mind." Willis was quite as unable to do away with wild ideas as were the most famous of his contemporaries. Gassendi, Boyle, Becher, and van Helmont believed in the growth of minerals (60q); Joseph Glanville and Richard Baxter believed in witches and spirits (16k); Boyle's therapeutic advices were at times quite barbarous (106c); Digby defended the famous sympathetic *weapon-salve* that had to be applied not to the wound, but to the weapon, thus healing the wound from a distance; despite Newton's praised scientific scepticism, his ideas on "spirit" were precisely those that had been published in 1621 by the pantheist, chymist, and audacious theorist, Sebastian Basso. (cf. 20) It should not be difficult to find unfounded theories and wild surmises in the writings of many other leading scientists of the age.

Willis had read a great deal (1) and was well aware of the "modern" theories because of the meetings of the *Vertuosi*. (14h) He constructed a complete theory of spontaneous reactions, i.e., of fermentation, from existent doctrines of practical chemistry, Iatrochemistry, and corpuscular theory. Ideas characteristic of Willis' theory can be found in the writings of earlier chemists, and the system most similar to the Willisian is that of Sebastian Basso, of 1621. Willis did not quite succeed in constructing a well-rounded and gapless system: the term *ferment* is not clearly defined in his book, the word is used with varied connotations, according to the context (above 48ff.). In the first chapter Willis refuses to accept the doctrine of the renewers of Democritus and Epicurus because of insufficient proof, but then he makes use of parts of this same doctrine to explain fire and light.

As Partington (60p) says, Willis was "one of the first to present a reasonable theory of fermentation." He succeeded in combining Iatrochemical, chymical, and corpuscular theories in a way that made them more attractive to the pioneers of experimental science. He thus made a very valuable contribution to the development of experimental science, which was then still struggling for survival against the forces of tradition. About a century later, in Diderot's encyclopédie, Willis appears as the leading authority on fermentation. (69) This fact, and the numerous reeditions of Willis' book, indicate that his influence upon the development of early biochemical thought should not be underrated. Willis' opinions on fermentation were taken up by Boerhaave (60q), who still believed in five chemical principles (99), and by Stahl. (60q) Their influence extends far into the beginnings of modern organic chemistry: Stahl's concept of the conveyance of molecular movement is, as Partington (60r) says, "an early theory of catalysis, and was much later developed further by Liebig. Actually it goes back to Willis." *

In "Of Fermentation," as in all his works, Willis puts together a choice of hypotheses, observations, and extrapolations which very often come close to what sci-

* The same in: Lieben (100b).

ence today thinks important. This is all the more astonishing since the majority of his basic theories must be found wrong today. When speaking of particles he understands them as Basso did, but contrary to Gassendi, not as indivisible entities: he is approaching a concept of molecular rather than atomic theory, thus interpreting one of the main ideas of his age more wisely than most of his contemporaries. The sentence: that we come into being, live, and die by the properties of ferments—will be affirmed by any present-day biologist. When Willis says that supervision of fermentation (in our language: of biochemical processes in the body) is the physician's duty, he is transcending the possibilities of his age and postulating something like today's laboratory-based medicine. His explanation of the solution of salt in water is suggestive of our theory of ion dissociation. Willis ascribes the excretion of urine to the effect of a ferment which could be aided by diuretics of a similar nature. In "Of the Urines" (2nd chapter) he describes the mechanisms of urine excretion in the kidneys as filtration and precipitation "through the force of a ferment," thus coming near to recent explanations of this function. His theory of light, though not original, represents the most advanced ideas before Hooke, Huyghens, and Newton. It is only from such bases as "Of Fermentation" that men like Hooke, Huyghens, and Newton could begin to build up modern science. (cf. 20)

Willis' description of the function of sexual hormones is very remarkable. Symonds (56) thinks that

Willis was the first to have a concept of a hormone; he was certainly the first to describe its effects with great care. "The seminal vessels and the genital parts abound more than other parts in fermentative particles. Here spirit, salt, and sulphur appear to be driven together, exalted and molded into sperm as into the noblest elixier. The principles thus active do not only ferment in the womb . . . , but they fill as with a living ferment the whole mass of blood everywhere in the body, so that it be more volatilized and effervesce more acidly. Therefore the face of women in whom the ferment of the womb behaves rightly is of flourishing and elegant color, and their warmth is strong and full; furthermore the mass of the blood is too opulent and has therefore to be evacuated each month by menstruation. If this fermentation from the womb fails, virgins and women become pale, as devoid of blood, short-winded, and are unable to move. In men also a fullness of warmth, great strength, deep voice, and the sprouting of body hair arise from the spermatic ferment: if it fails men become effeminate, the voice high, the warmth feeble, the beard hopeless." (AA, 5, p. 13) With these sentences (which he elaborates upon in "Specimen . . . ," 1667, see below p. 125) Willis at least anticipates the doctrine of Théophile Bordeu, who is said to have been the first describing the action of the sexual hormones (in 1775: 100c, 104). Bordeu simply identifies the internal secretion with the sperm, whereas Willis speaks of a separate tincture (in "Specimen") that is conveyed everywhere by the blood.

OF FEVERS

This book is founded upon Willis' case histories of febrile diseases from continuous fevers. He describes quartan, tertian, and quotidian intermittent fever. The continuous fevers are: putrid fever, ephemeral fever, pestilential, or malignant fevers (such as the plague), smallpox, puerperal and lactation fever, and mastitis, and the epidemic fevers. Willis attempts to give new explanations of these diseases in the terms of his doctrine of fermentation.

As he says in the preface, he wants to compare his observations one to another, and to "adapt general Notions from particular events." (G) He assumes that the blood is a mixture of the five chymical principles: spirit, sulphur, salt, water, and earth, which may be separated by distillation. The production of blood out of nutrient humor, as well as the excretion of wastes from the blood, are compared to the fermentation of wine, and blood coagulation is to be understood in the same way as the curdling of milk. (AB, 1) There is a natural and a preternatural kind of fermentation in blood. Production of blood, activation of blood in the heart, and excretion of wastes are natural fermentations. Through the influence of alien matter or through exalted activity of one of the normal constituents a preternatural fermentation may arise in the blood, causing the phenomena of fever: "inordinate motion of the blood, excessive effervescence of the blood, with heat, thirst, and other symptoms, that variously disturb the natural economy." (AB, 3)

"Of Fevers" as a whole has been forgotten, but some achievements of the book are still noted in medical history. The accurate records of intermittent fevers kept by Willis are cited by Ackerknecht (90) as a reliable source for the importance of Malaria in seventeenth century England. Zinsser (59) regards Willis' description of camp fever (febris castrensis) as the earliest proof of the existence of typhus fever in England. According to Creighton's "History of Epidemics in Britain" Willis' account of three consecutive epidemics in 1657 and 1658 is "the first systematic piece of epidemiology written in England," and "the middle epidemic of the three was one of influenza." (91) Willis' clinical picture of puerperal fever has been called excellent (94), and Peckham (92a) says that "Willis was the first to suggest anything resembling a modern terminology of the condition." The chapters about typhoid fever (febris putrida, AB. 9, 10) and the typhus (febres pestilentes, ac malignae in specie, AB. 14) have been reprinted in part by R. H. Major in his "Classic Descriptions of Diseases." (93a)

These outstanding observations were used by Willis as foundations for his theories about the origin of febrile diseases. Willis ascribed the fevers to chemical disorders of the blood, adapting his theory of fermentation in order to account for the various symptoms. In intermittent fevers the blood is chemically changed because of changes in the seasons, in local climate (coeli constitutio), or in the constitution of the body. Such distempers may render the blood more acid, bitter, or harsh. The blood thus becomes unable to assimilate the nutrient humor that comes from the intestines: the nutrient humor acts as an alien matter and disturbs the fermentative balance of the blood. After having reached critical mass, the alien, or morbific, matter incites the blood into an unnatural fermentation that continues until the alien matter is subdued or excreted. The difference in rhythm between quotidian, tertian, and quartan fever results from the chemical difference between the distempers that cause them. If the blood becomes bitter (acris) only half of the nutrient humor can be assimilated in one twenty-four-hour period of digestion; the other half stays in the blood as an alien matter; critical mass is reached after 48 hours, fever begins on the third day, and the result is a tertian fever. If the blood is harsh and salty (austera et pontica) only one third of the nutrient humor is left unassimilated, critical mass is reached in 72 hours, and fever begins on the fourth day, as in quartan fever. If a more severe distemper makes the blood acid (acida), most of the nutrient humor turns into fever matter, and fever keeps reappearing daily, as in a quotidian.

Only a few febrile diseases are contagious. The most contagious are the malignant and pestilential fevers, such as typhus and the plague. In measles and smallpox individual predisposition is far more important than infection by a *contagium* that can but initiate the disease. A *contagium* is "a force . . . by means of which a disease dwelling in a body produces a similar disease in another body." (AB), 12) The *contagium* consists of emanations of particles. In plague, for instance, it is a poison that combines with the spirits in the body. The malignant and putrid fevers (AB. 9, 10, 14), mainly typhus and typhoid fever, result from an excess of sulphur in the body; by the overbalance of sulphur the amount of saline particles in the blood is reduced. (AB. 9) Putrid and epidemic fevers result from coincidences of climate, body constitution, and further environmental factors. Puerperal fever also is not caused by infection, but comes from a greater fermentability of the blood because of the accumulated menstruations, and because of lesions of the womb in childbirth (à partu malae uteri affectiones). Bad eating habits and exposure to cold may be accidental causes.

Harvey's description of blood circulation has given a new foundation to medicine. This is the reason Willis gives for his enterprise of taking up again a subject seemingly as exhausted as the fevers. (AB, preface) Willis explains his views with the easy confidence so typical of advocates of progress through the ages. He states that the most important activities in blood have now been discovered: blood is the same humor everywhere throughout the body, everywhere moving unceasingly in the same circulation: the products of intestinal digestion are continuously supplied to it as a nutrient humor, and the wastes are continuously separated fom it by the spleen (as black bile), the liver (yellow bile), and the solid parts (as lymph, or phlegm).

The most important step in the utilisation of the nutrient humor is its assimilation to blood, that is, the production of blood out of the nutrient humor, which takes place in the blood as it is circulating in the vessels. The most important part of this process is the activation of the natural fermentation of blood in the heart by a ferment (according to Hogelandus) or an inner fire (according to Descartes). Because of these results the basic conviction of traditional medicine has become untenable: of the four humors, yellow bile, black bile, phlegm, and blood, three are but waste products that have to be continuously eliminated from the blood, and thus cannot be mistaken for constituents of blood. (AB,1) There are no hiding places from which these three humors could suddenly break out and cause diseases. The traditional explanation of the intermittent fevers is thus disproved. In the place of the obsolete Galenic humors Willis substitutes blood, nervous humor (a concept adopted from Glisson and Wharton) and a serous humor "continuously separated from blood." Willis says that a third of all humanity still falls a victim to the fevers: in the face of the new truths further treatment based on obsolete ideas cannot be justified any more.

In "Of Fevers" Willis gives very little detailed therapeutic advice, confining himself to general indications. According to the various clinical situations described, he recommends one or more of the following classes of remedies: vomitives, purgatives, sudorifics, digestives, narcotics, cardiacs, pectorals, antipyretics, antipyretics for local use, and bleeding. Most important among these therapeutic measures is evacuation by purgatives, sudorifics, vomitives, and bleeding. By evacuation the blood can be rid of harmful alien matter or of excessive chemical principles. But Willis often advises the reader to be cautious. He warns against the use of strong vomitives, purgatives, and cardiacs in weakened patients. He says that decisions for such drastic therapy should be based upon evaluation of pulse and urine, and especially of the constitution of the patient. Willis' concept of body constitution is not much different from that of traditional medicine, but he does not accept the idea that the four constitutions result from a predominance of one Galenic humor above the others.

In the therapy of intermittent fevers Willis distinguishes a natural from an artificial way of cure. An intermittent fever may be cured in a natural way, either by a change in the chemical *tuning* of the blood through the influence of the disease, or through a change in climate. The empirical remedies of quacks and old women (remedia Empirica ab agyrtis, aut mulierculis petita) are often more useful for artificial cures than those of school medicine (dogmatica). The treatment of traditional medicine consists in drastic evacuation by vomitives, purgatives, and bleeding, by which "the patients are miserably tortured, and the disease is seldom vanquished . . ." (AB, 4) Willis believes that the quacks' remedies act more or less as specifics. He suggests the following course of treatments:

1. Restoration of the right chemical tuning of the blood by evacuation, digestives, and, above all, change in climate. There is no reason for an evacuation except at the beginning of the disease.
2. Correction of the nutrient humor through light and limited diet, and fasting shortly before the onset of a paroxysm.
3. Suppression of the paroxysm by antipyretics shortly before its onset. These antipyretics are the salts, herbs, even jewels as used by several kinds of quacks.

Willis gives a detailed account of only one drug: "that Peruvian bark," quinine. As Fischer (114) writes, general acceptance of the use of quinine in England goes back to the encouraging statements about it by Willis, Sydenham, and Morton. Fischer adds that Willis contributed most to the spreading of the bark. Since Morton's publications appeared later than those of Willis and Sydenham, the chronology of the opinions of the latter two should be considered. Willis mentions the use of the bark for the cure of quartan fever in the first edition of 1659, admits its restraining action upon the febrile fermentation in the second edition of the same year, but remarks that it is no certain cure: in the third edition of 1662 he says that there is no theory to explain its action. (60p) In the last version (e.g. Amsterdam 1669) half a chapter is devoted to quinine. Willis still attempts to interpret the success of quinine therapy as evidence for the rightness of his advice (as outlined above), but he also has to concede that quinine, unlike all other antipyretics, can suppress more than one paroxysm even if it is given only once. He thinks that the bark incites the blood into a new kind of fermentation that keeps it from taking up the effervescence of fever. But this effect often passes quickly. There is no final explanation because no drug of similar potency has been found until now: a general explanation cannot rightly be adapted to only one experiment. Willis predicts that in the future other remedies of similar efficiency will be found. From the fact of the existence of quinine it is to be inferred that other potent specifics must exist *in rerum natura*. (AB, 6) Sydenham (cf. 58) has been rather more reluctant to acknowledge the usefulness of quinine. In 1666, when Willis had already published his first cautious evaluations of the drug and was about to grasp the full significance of this first real specific, Sydenham still accused it of having caused several deaths by interrupting the natural development of the disease. (58)

The theories in "Of Fevers" are often founded upon recent results of outstanding scientists. Willis writes that blood continuously assimilates new constituents from the nutrient humor, that the liver has no part in this production of blood, that the wornout parts of the blood are continuously eliminated and excreted in the spleen as black bile, and in the liver, as yellow bile. This is an exact outline of the hypotheses of Rudbeck and Bartholinus of 1653, corresponding to the opinions of Pecquet and Glisson which were published after "Of Fevers". (cf. Mani, 9, and Glisson, 84) In "Of the

Urines" (AC, 2) Willis combines a theory of Harvey with one of Bartholinus: observing that, very soon after copious drinking, great quantities of watery urine are voided, he concludes that there must be a more direct way from the intestines into the blood besides the lacteals. He correctly assumes that the thinner ("watery-spirituous") part of the nutrient juice passes directly into the branches of the portal vein through the spongy walls of the stomach and intestines, whereas the thicker part is conducted into the upper vena cava by way of the lacteals.

Some of Willis' theories are quite suggestive of doctrines that became established centuries later. According to "Of Fevers" the contagious agent, or *contagium,* manages to survive between two consecutive epidemics by transforming other particles outside the human body into particles similar to itself, which are able to subsist for a long time in hidden foci, and even to increase in numbers and in potency, until they finally infest another appropriate subject (idoneum subjectum). In this brilliant extrapolation Willis anticipates the concepts of intermediate host, and of change in virulence through changing hosts. Though Lancisi later found a similar explanation for malaria, these ideas have been substantiated only in the late nineteenth and twentieth centuries.

The first chapter of Willis' "Of Fevers," entitled "Anatomy of the Blood," contains the earliest account of the biochemical importance of protein. Willis compares the coagulation of blood to the curdling of milk.

He says that the serous liquid that is left above the clotted parts can be further coagulated: if it is heated it becomes thick "like the white of a slightly cooked egg," and if it is mixed with acid it is precipitated as a white coagulum.* He then proceeds to give a clear description of hypoproteinemia in dropsy: ". . . there is sometimes an excess [of the watery liquid] for instance in those suffering from dropsy, and it does not wholly turn into a white coagulum, when heated. . . ."** In "Of the Urines" (AC, 3) he ventures to say that in the blood circulating in the vessels a glutinous humor is produced which changes into minute filaments that are then inserted into the pores and interstices of the solid parts, where they serve as materials for their growth.*** Willis was quite aware of the importance of these views: he described them again as a whole in his "Anatomy of the Brain." (B, 20, p. 255 f.)

Willis was of course not the only medical author of his century that used the expression "ovi albumen"—white of eggs—to illustrate physiological observations.

* ". . . ita liquor hic sanguini innatans, si veligni exponatur, instar albuminis ovi parum cocti inspissatur, vel si liquor acidus ei suffundatur, in coagulum album praecipitabitur" (AA, 1, p. 50). The discovery of the coagulation of plasma is usually attributed to William Hewitt (1777) (cf. Rotschuh, 96).

** ". . . latex aquosus aliquando superabundat; prout in hydropicis; nec totus in coagulum album a calore facessit . . ." (loc. cit).

*** "Quamdiu sanguinis massa sero, & humore alibili perfusa, in vasis continuo circulatur, ex ea succus quidam nutritius perpetua digestione elaboratur; qui in nutrimentum solidis partibus continuo adponendum facessit; hic primo in humorem glutinosum, instar ovi albuminis, postea in tenuia filamenta excoquitur, quae poris, & spatiolis solidarum partium intertexta, iis novae usque substantiae accretionem praebent . . ." (AC, 3, 156; cf. B, 20, 255 f.).

At about the same time Giovanni Alfonso Borelli (60s) compared blood coagulation to milk curdling and described a glutinous humor in the blood that coagulated in a fibrous form, using the word "ovi albumen" for the liquid left above the clotted parts. But only Willis formulated his ideas about what we call protein in the same way as the men who rediscovered it in the nineteenth century.

In 1840 Leroux described a *glue* as the most nutritious substance (Willis: a glutinous humor, similar to the white of eggs, that serves the growth of the solid parts). Justus von Liebig is said to have been led, like Willis, by a "divinatory scientific imagination." He "[devoured] every book on chemistry he could get" (97), and his explanation of fermentation goes back to Willis (60r). In 1842 Liebig was the first to call protein the most important plastic material in the organism. In the very same year he wrote that the oxydation of nutritive matter takes place in the blood—exactly what Willis had said, although in other words, in his "De Sanguinis Incalescentia" of 1670. (cf. below p. 142ff.) In 1852 P. Panum and Jakob Moleschott described a "serum casein" or "cheese matter" (Moleschott) in the blood, which is generally taken for the first reference to serum protein:* but Willis already gives "buttery and caseous parts . . . as in milk serum" as reasons for the coagulation of blood serum.

* From: Rothschuh (96), and also from Lieben, "Geschichte der physiologischen Chemie" (100a).

ORIGINS

Like "Of Fermentation," "Of Fevers" is often said to belong to the school of van Helmont, or of Sylvius. No proof for these assumptions can be found in the work. General similarities, like the fact that these three authors alike compare processes in the human body to the fermentation of wine, or their common tendency to stress the importance of digestion, can only prove their belonging to the great movement of Iatrochemistry. But there are decisive differences between their explanations of basic phenomena. Van Helmont states that the seat of fevers is in the intestines and in their vessels, and he says that only sudorifics are of any use against fevers (febrium doctrina inaudita, first ed. 1642, quoted here from (98)). Willis places the origin of fevers in the blood, and he recommends a far more refined, though probably not more effective therapy. Like Willis, Descartes, and many other contemporaries, Sylvius believes in an activation of blood in the heart. But Sylvius thinks that blood is activated in the heart by an effervescence of alcaline bile and acid lymph; according to his own definition, this cannot be called a fermentative process, and it has nothing to do with an internal fire. Sylvius believes that bile is an important physiological constituent of blood, essential for the continuance of life, whereas Willis regards bile as a mere waste product that must be eliminated. (cf. above p. 72) (Sylvius, Disp. Med. X, first ed. 1663 (63), cit. here from (82b) Willis' "Of Fevers" is founded upon his own observations and his own chemical system. We have attempted to show that there are very few concepts that his chemical system has in common with those of Sylvius and van Helmont. (cf. above p. 57ff.) On the other hand, Willis certainly adopted opinions and ideas about his fevers from a variety of sources: Hippocrates (influence of climate, natural way of cure, importance of first-hand observation), Harvey (circulation, ingestion of nutrient humor), Glisson and Wharton (nervous humor), Rudbeck and Bartholin (ingestion of nutrient humor, lymphatic system), Descartes and Hogelandus (process of activation of blood in the heart), and Sennert (puerperal fever due to retention of menses in pregnancy).

EVALUATION

"Of Fevers" is conspicuous among contemporary English medical books for its aggressiveness. Far from looking for a compromise with Galenic medicine and Aristotelian learning, Willis expressly denounces them as obsolete. Harvey, for instance, never attempted to question the supreme authority of Aristotle, and Glisson—who had actually infected the venerable disputations at Cambridge with scientific ideas (26), and who, like Willis, had accepted the revolutionary concepts of the chymists—did his best to reconcile the chymical system with traditional humoral pathology (Anatomia Hepatis, 1659, (84) . Among the English physicians of note only Sydenham has surpassed Willis' aggressiveness, and Sydenham's first book has so much in common with "Of Fevers" that it must to some extent depend from it.

When compared with contemporary writings about the same subject, e.g. van Helmont's (98), Sylvius' (82b), or Sydenham's (58, 101), "Of Fevers" appears to be more systematic and richer in content. The quality of the representation of diseases is often on a level with the good textbooks of the late nineteenth century, and Willis' theories, though highstrung and often extremely speculative, sometimes anticipate results of later generations. The numerous reeditions show that the book was quite successful. Even O'Meara, in his critical treatise, calls it "that famous doctrine of the Fevers" (praeclara illa Febrium doctrina (58)). "Of Fevers" was to be a classic for several generations; it was one of the sources that helped to fill medical compendia (102), and in 1792 Mathias von Sallaba, one of Mozart's physicians, still found it indispensable to quote several pages from the book. (165) Conditions for the success of the work were extremely favorable, since shortly after its publication the fight between traditional and Iatrochemical medicine attracted much attention both in England and on the Continent; and as an Oxford professor, a leader of Iatrochemistry, an approved partisan of victorious Royalism and of the triumphant Anglican Church, and a distinguished pioneer of the *new science,* Willis' position as an authority was fortified on every side.

IN THE WAKE: SYDENHAM

Sydenham's revolutionary attitude is distinctly suggestive of that of Willis. But Sydenham was an adherent of the losing party, a member of a church that was nearly outlawed, he despised the chymists (101d), his relations to the movement of the *new science* were not good; when he first appeared as a writer he was not in a position that favored the advancement of new ideas. It was easier for him to advance opinions and tendencies that had been already successfully introduced by Willis.

Willis writes in the preface to "Of Fevers," "And if the descendants, led by the example of Hippocrates, had but taken up again his observations and experiments, medical art would have grown to be of more use to the ailing, better, and more beautiful."* Willis says in the same preface that he has founded his book upon bedside observations and their inductive interpretation. His descriptions of diseases and his diary (175) prove that he used these methods. But Sydenham is called "the English Hippocrates," because he used to appeal to the authority of Hippocrates (101b),

* Atque si, Hippocratis exemplo ducti, posteri ejus observationes tantum, & experimenta recoluissent, proculdubio ars Medica cum majori aegrotantium fructu, melius & ornatius accrevisset (AB).

and because "Sydenham's greatness is in his clinical observations," direct observation being of paramount importance in his work. (84) Following Hippocrates, Willis prefers *natural to artificial* cures in the therapy of intermittent fevers: so does Sydenham. (101c) In his descriptions of epidemics, "the first systematic piece of epidemiology written in England" (91) , Willis stresses the importance of the climate. He concludes that epidemic fevers arise from a "febrile diathesis, or predisposition, that has been slowly impressed into our bodies before [the epidemic] because of intemperate climate . . ."*, the climate of certain seasons and places (tempestas, coeli constitutio) , which influences the body by means of the air. The whole idea of Sydenham's famous "Constitutio Epidemica" is found in Willis' book; later it became the leitmotiv of epidemiological studies until the 19th century.

Sydenham is generally regarded as the champion of medical scepticism, and he used to ascribe his knowledge to his own experience; it may appear strange that he had to take his most cherished ideas from Willis, who is often mistaken for his antipode, deeply stuck in a heap of preconceived opinions. But Sydenham did more than that, he actually adopted most of Willis' iatrochemical explanation of intermittent fevers, including the notion of a fermentation in the blood that can be compared to those in cider, beer, and wine (58),

* ". . . à diathesi, seu praedispositione quadam febrili, propter anni intemperiem antehac paulatim corporibus nostris impressa . . ."

and a simplified theory of fermentability. In fact, even Sydenham's credo of medical scepticism is very similar to a sentence from Willis' "Of Fermentation." Willis wrote: "Nightblind and dullwitted, I leave the more accurate [questions] to those of sharper view (lynceis): I am content to know what the external senses provide to the reasoning mind; to wit, I readily profess that I do not want to fabricate or to dream of a philosophy." (AA, 1, p. 2)* And Sydenham wrote in 1666 (58), "I do not crave the name of a philosopher; and those who believe that they deserve that title, and perhaps will think it necessary to blame me by this name—although I have not attempted to break into these secrets: those I admonish to try their forces in other works of nature that confront us everywhere, before bringing action against others."**

Sydenham cannot be accused of plagiarizing. Among his many talents he had the gift of finding what he needed, and he was lucky enough to have been born in the time of Willis. He succeeded in changing parts of Willis' system into something more palatable to unpretentious readers, and his own observations are as valuable as those of Willis. But the merit for introduc-

* Lusciosus ego atque hebes, lynceis accuratiora relinquo; eatenus sapere contentus, quousque rationi sensus externi operam praestitere; procudere enim, aut somniare philosophiam me nolle lubens profiteor.

** Ego Philosophi nomen non ambio; & qui titulum illum se mereri existimant, atque me fortassis hoc nomine culpandum putabunt, quòd in haec penetralia non irrumpere conatus sim; moneo illos, ut in aliis naturae operibus, quae ubique nobis obversantur, vires suas experiri velint, antequam aliis dicam scribant (58, Methodus Curandi Febres, p. 71).

ing firsthand observation as a guiding principle into medicine does not belong to Sydenham. In the first place it belongs to Thomas Willis' "Of Fevers."

CEREBRI ANATOME

This book (B) was published in London in 1664. In 1665 it was favorably reviewed in the very first scientific journal known to us, the "Journal des Sçavans," founded in the same year. (156) Also in 1665 it was criticized by Nicolaus Steno in his famous discourse on the anatomy of the brain. (176)

"Cerebri Anatome" is the result of a fullfledged research project realized by a team under Willis' direction. It contains results from embryology, morbid (pathologic) anatomy, clinical observation (105b), animal experiments (B 24, p. 324), anatomical dye injection (B 7, p. 97), microscopy (B 19, p. 241 f.), and comparative anatomy. Willis says, " . . . since I shall point out the similarities and differences that appear when we compare the observed parts in various animals, comparing these to other animals and to Man: Surely it will be possible out of this compared anatomy, not only to detect the faculties and uses of each organ, but also the traces, influences, and hidden ways of action of the sensitive soul." (B 1, p. 4) He thus states that he hopes to explain the complete anatomy and physiology of the nervous system, and to obtain a physical foundation for psychology. The sensitive soul, in Willis' terminology, is the totality of the functional elements of the whole nervous system, that is, the sum of the animal spirits. Together with the vital, or life-soul, the totality of the life-flame in the blood, the sensitive soul constitutes the body-soul. The body-soul is the perceptive and motive principle in all animals. In Man it is dominated by the rational soul which is capable of ample reasoning, abstract thinking, and conscious will. The brain is the primary seat of the corporeal soul in brutes, and of the rational soul in man.

Willis' research team consisted of his long-time assistant Richard Lower, the astronomer and architect Christopher Wren, and Dr. Thomas Millington, a physician who later succeeded Willis as Sedleian professor. Willis acknowledges their part in the work as follows: "But in order to complete this work more accurately, I would not blush to make use of the helping hands of others, since I myself had not enough time, and perhaps not enough force [to do it] by my efforts alone." (Preface to (B))

Thanks to Lower's help, Willis says, scarcely a day passed without some anatomical investigation. It was Lower who with indefatigable industry pursued every nerve up to its finest and most intricate ramifications, it was Lower who drew the diagrams of nerves and blood vessels for the book, and who verified their accuracy by means of control dissections. Wren and Millington often assisted at the dissections of Willis and Lower. Day after day Willis discussed his observations and conjectures with Millington. In spite of his "singular humanity," Christopher Wren (then Savilian Professor of Astronomy) was not above drawing illustrations of the brain and calvary "with his most erudite hands."

It is only in his books devoted to the nervous system that Willis brings in theological arguments. In the dedication of "Cerebri Anatome" (to Gilbert Sheldon, Archbishop of Canterbury) he states that a *philosopher* who lacks good Christian faith must needs be a fake. In the same dedication he condemns those mechanistic interpretations of nature that lead to a loss of faith. Probably for the same reasons Willis felt compelled to justify his method of investigating the human brain, and human psychology, by means of comparative anatomy. Human corpses, he argues, cannot be had at all times of the year, the "immense bulk of the human brain itself" is an obstacle to research; in most of the quadrupedes, as in the dog, the calf, the swine, the brain is not so very different from the human one except for its size; this similarity comes from the common origin of those animals (animalia; man and brutes as distinguished from plants and inanimate matter). According to the Genesis they have been created on the same day; whereas fish and fowl were made the day before. Consequently there is a great difference between the brains of man and quadrupedes on the one hand, and those of fish and birds on the other. (B 1, p. 3 ff.)

Since a detailed review of "Cerebri Anatome" would

be beyond the scope of this book, we shall follow the excellent summary given by Jules Soury. (105a)

In the brain as in the cerebellum, Willis distinguishes cortical from medullary substance (white matter). In the cortical substance the animal spirits—the carriers of the activities of the nervous system—are produced out of the arterial blood. They are received by the white matter which resembles that of the mel dulla and spinal cord. There they are distributed and take up their functions. Interruptions of the white matter result in a loss of action in the disconnected parts which cannot receive any more spirits. The center of the brain (cerebri meditullia) is a reservoir where the spirits are kept in great quantities in order to serve the activities of the rational soul. From the center of the brain they flow down into the medulla and the spinal cord, from thence into the nerves and the sensory parts, into the various parts that perform voluntary motions, and the acts of vegetative life.

The animal spirits are produced by a kind of distillation in the cortex. Arterial blood is conveyed to the grey cortex through arteries that serve as distillatory organs. The blood passing through these vessels is separated from its more coarse and inactive (chymical) parts which are taken into the veins as "cruor." The serum is gathered by the glands which are found everywhere in the neighborhood of the blood vessels of the pia mater. Thus only the purer, *spirituous* part of the blood is brought into the cortex. The blood vessels of the entire brain are interconnected so that every deficiency of a vessel may be compensated by the next one.

Willis states that the brain itself has neither sensibility nor motility, unlike the meninges, which have both. Headache is explained by the sensibility of the meninges. The sinuses of the dura mater are in effect so many water baths that convey the necessary heat for the distillation of the spirits.

The human brain is parted into two hemispheres, each of which is again divided into an anterior and a posterior lobe by a branch of the carotid artery. The whole surface of the brain consists of gyri and convolutions: thus there is room for a far greater expanse of cortex than under a flat and even surface. The convolutions can be compared to pigeonholes and depots where the species or impressions of sensible things are stored, and from whence they may be evoked upon suitable occasions. The convolutions are more numerous and of greater size in man than in all other animals, as Willis believes, "because of the various and multiple acts of (his) superior facilities. . . . In the lesser quadrupedes, as in birds and fish, the flat and even surface of the brain is completely devoid of gyri and bends, therefore such animals understand, or learn through imitation fewer things, and mostly from only one category." (directly from B 10, p. 125)

(Continued according to Soury.) The medulla is the common stem of cerebrum and cerebellum, both of which have been regarded as mere appendages of the medullary tract. In Willis' view the pattern of production and distribution of the spirits proves that cerebrum and cerebellum are predominant over the medullary tract. The cerebrum is the primary seat of the rational soul in man, and of the sensitive soul in animals. It is the source of movements and ideas. The animal activities come from the cerebrum, whereas the *natural* functions like the sensations, movements, passions, instincts, or impulses also depend to some extent from the cerebrum, but are generated in the cerebellum and in the medulla.

The corpus callosum consists of white matter It receives medullary fibres coming from all the convolutions. It seems to be intended as a kind of market place (emporium). It is here that the recently produced spirits gather from every side. Here they stay awhile and begin to perform their functions, either serving imagination or proceeding into the crura of the medulla, causing movements according to appetite in the spinal cord, and in the entrails.

The pineal body is not the seat of the soul. Though in general Willis seldom cites the names of authors, he mentions Descartes with whom he does not agree in that respect. The structure is found to be quite developed in all animals including fish, i.e. in all the vertebrates. Willis is convinced that it must have a necessary function. However it cannot have anything to do with sensory or intellectual functions since in animals with a poor imagination and memory it is found to be more developed than in man. The pineal body has the same function as the other glands which are found in the neighborhood of the vascular plexus, namely, to receive serous humors coming from the arterial blood, which are then reabsorbed by the veins or conveyed outward by lymphatic vessels.

In Antiquity and in the Middle Ages high functions have been ascribed to the ventricles. According to Willis, no more can be said about them than about the empty space that astronomers find in the hollow of the spheres. They are but drains for the excremental fluids of the brain. Willis still believes that the liquid from the ventricles proceeds through the infundibulum into the pituitary, which collects them and passes them on to blood vessels and lymphatic vessels. He sees a further way of drainage in the olfactory nerves which divert the liquids into the nose through the holes in the cribriform bone.

The medulla begins where the corpus callosum ends; it is the thoroughfare for the spirits coming from cerebrum and cerebellum, and proceeding into the nervous parts everywhere in the body. The corpora striata are the upper ends of the crura of the medulla; they are joined to the corpus callosum. They contain tracts leading from the cerebrum to the medulla, and vice versa. They are rest houses which receive the spirits from everywhere and send them out in all directions—the place where the pictures, or phantasms, of sensible things coming from the sensory organs arrive through the nerve canals. The pictures of phantasms arriving here are the results of actions of dispersed particles that influence the spirits in the nerves of the organs. In the corpora striata the impressions from the inner and outer organs modify one another. It is here that perceptions of the sensory impression takes place, which we mistake for a peripheral process. According to its intensity, a sensory impression may not pass beyond the corpora striata, reflecting itself as involuntary local movements; or it may proceed to the cortex through the corpus callosum. When pain arises at some spot on our body while we are asleep, we at once take our hand to the painful spot and rub it without becoming conscious of it.

This is a clear description of reflex action, which is a term coined by Willis in "Cerebri Anatome," and defined as follows: A movement is reflex if it depends from a previous sensation, and is turned back at once. (Motus est reflexus qui a sensione praevia dependens illico retorquetur.) (105c)

The corpora striata are the sensorium commune, the proton aistheterion of Aristotle. Morbid (pathologic) anatomy proves that the voluntary motor impulses also come from the corpora striata; in brains of patients that have been paralyzed for a long time the striata are found to be less firm than the other parts.

If a sensory impression does not pass beyond the striata, its image may already be viewed at that level by the rational soul. It can be completely comprehended only in the corpus callosum, where imagination succeeds sensory apprehension. On this plane the image may still be reflected as local movement.

When a sensory impression reaches the cortex through the medullary substance it ebbs away like a wave, but traces remain in the folds of the cortex, and constitute memory and reminiscence. In Willis' view memory depends so much on imagination that it appears to be but a reflex action of imagination.

The only seat of memory and imagination is the brain. When a trace of a sensory impression is later reflected again, it evokes the memory of the sensed object. Every sensory impression that reaches the folds of the cortex may stir up the images hidden there. Together with imagination, such a memory can cause affective states and local movements depending from these. If the sensory impression contained in imagination is accompanied by the feeling of something good to be aspired after or something bad to be avoided, the spirits at once transmit orders for the necessary movements.

For Willis, as for Galen, the optic layers are the origins of the optic nerves. Their white matter begins where the striata end. The junction and redivision of the optic nerves serve to identify the visual images of both nerves, and to avoid double vision.

Willis is especially intrigued by the comparative anatomy of the quadrigeminate bodies. Out of the passage from the cerebrum to the medulla impulses are diverted to the cerebellum by way of the quadrigeminate bodies: thus the passions (emotions, affects) influence the involuntary functions. The quadrigeminate bodies serve mainly to convey the natural impulses from the cerebellum to the cerebrum where they cause moods that result in more or less purposeful movements.

Quite like the cerebrum, which causes voluntary and conscious movements by emitting spirits into the nervous system, the cerebellum produces the spirits needed for the involuntary motions like heartbeat, respiration, movement of the intestine, i.e. for all those movements which take place in a regular fashion without our becoming conscious of them, and even against our will. While the gyri of the cerebrum are irregular and varied, the folds and lamellas of the cerebellum are laid out in a certain order. As in an artificial automaton the spirits in the cerebellum keep flowing without a driver (auriga) directing and moderating their movements. The spirits distilled here are used but for established purposes. Willis states that the structure of the cerebellum, contrary to that of the cerebrum, is in many animals nearly similar to the human one. In the cerebellum the flow and distribution of the spirits is even and uninterrupted, whereas in the cerebrum it is quite as irregular as the actions originating there. Violent emotions from the cerebrum may change the regular processes in the inner organs, and certain states of the inner organs may again influence the cerebrum in a way that induces it to change, through the cerebellum, the involuntary functions of the inner organs. All these automatic, or involuntary motions depend on a natural memory located in the cerebellum. Voluntary and involuntary movements are transmitted through separate nerves. The function of the cerebrum depends from that of the cerebellum because the supply of spirituous arterial blood is guaranteed by the cerebellum, which controls the natural functions.

The quadrigeminate bodies are the anterior, the annular protuberance (pons) the posterior appendix of the cerebellum. Like the quadrigeminates, the pons is a conductive part: in both directions it joins the cerebellum to the natural organs, i.e. the vegetative organs. The spirits in the pons also commit emotional movements to the inner organs. The cranial nerves originating from the pons and cerebellum do the same thing; since their spirits come from the cerebellum, they only transmit involuntary movements and sensations.

Willis formulates the following law of comparative anatomy: in animals with a predominance of instinct and scarcity of emotions, or passions, as in sheep, cattle, goats, and swine, the pons is small, and the quadrigeminates are large. In those animals where intelligence dominates the instincts, and where emotions are strong, the relation is reversed. In the monkey this law is found to hold true: dissecting a cercopithecus, Willis found pons and quadrigeminates similar to those of man in form and respective size. He calls the quadrigeminates the main organs of the natural instincts. Since their volume and their complexity must be related to their function, as it is the case with every organ, the importance of the instincts in quadrupedes can be evaluated from their aspect. The same is true of the proportions of the pituitary. Willis remarks that the olfactory nerves in man are very much thinner than in quadrupedes with a good sense of smell.

The spinal cord is the common channel through which the spirits flow from the brain into the nerves. Like the medulla it consists of innumerable canals. Its volume increases at those levels where diverting canals are most numerous: where the nerves branch away to the arms and legs. The cortices of cerebrum and cerebellum may be taken as the roots of the medullary tree, its trunk would then be the whole white matter, the nerves and nerve fibers its branches, twigs and leaves.

Movement and sensation depend on the spirits. They move about in the nervous—and nutrient—juice which, like the spirits, is produced in the cerebrum and cerebellum. The nervous juice is more viscous and more sulphurous than the spirits, which are extremely volatile; it serves as the vehicle in which they move. Through the nerve canals, the nervous juice irrigates all the nerves; nutrition and growth of all parts of the body depend on it. That is why loss of motility and sensibility in paralysis is soon followed by muscular atrophy. The nutritive matter is distributed by the arteries in the whole body. Only through the influence of the nervous juice, which is a ferment, nutritive matter is finally changed into nutriment, and then assimilated. So much from Jules Soury.

CRANIAL NERVES

In "Cerebri Anatome" Willis gives a new classification of the cranial nerves:

I. olfactorius, II. opticus, III oculomotorius, IV. trochlearis (Willis: patheticus), V. trigeminus (Willis: trifacialis), VI. abducens. VII. facialis and statoacusticus (Willis: par auditorium, consisting of a ramus durus-facialis, and a ramus mollis-acusticus, as in Galen), VIII. vagus, accessorius, glossopharyngicus (Willis: par actavum), and IX. hypoglossus. (54, 112) This system was generally accepted: it remained in use until the current system, erroneously ascribed to Soemmering, was introduced. (106a, 107, cf. 157) In English speaking countries it was still taught in universities in the second half of the nineteenth century. (6, 54)

In this context Willis gave the first description and illustration of the accessory as an independent nerve. (54, 108) "The historical merit of Willis' classification of the cranial nerves," say Hierons/Meyer (108), "can be judged correctly only against the background of the prevailing confusion among his contemporaries, and immediate predecessors . . . "

THE AUTONOMIC NERVOUS SYSTEM

The involuntary functions of the vagus complex and the sympathetic nerves (which he calls "intercostales") are of extreme importance to Willis. They are extensively discussed in his books dealing with the nervous system. Willis substituted for the ancient view of the heart as the center of emotions the theory of an involuntary or autonomic nervous system governed by the cerebellum: "[he] . . . must be considered one of the chief founders of the concept of the autonomic nervous system and its cerebral control . . . " (108, citing D. Sheehan)

Willis' contribution to the understanding of the sympathetic nerve has been discussed by Hierons and Meyer. (108) They conclude that, while the evolution of this knowledge was gradual, and Vesal deserved the credit for publishing the first illustration of the sympathetic nerve, Eustachius and Willis were "the only anatomists of this whole period who have given clear illustrations of two separate nerves" instead of considering the sympathetic as part of the vagus. Eustachius and Willis both give the sympathetic a cranial origin, Eustachius deriving it from the VI. nerve, Willis from the V. and VI. nerves; since the tables of Eustachius were discovered and published only seventy years after the publication of "Cerebri Anatome," Willis appears to have reached his opinion by convergent reasoning rather than through the influence of Eustachius' ideas. (108)

Together with the tables of Eustachius, the tables IX and X of "Cerebri Anatome" are judged the best illustrations of the peripheral autonomic nervous system up to the beginning of the eighteenth century (108);

they show the topographical relations to the visceral organs, and they also contain Willis' observation that in lower animals the vagus is more important than the sympathetic, an observation repeated by Gaskell in 1916, without reference to Willis. (108) Willis says in the preface, that they were drawn and verified by Richard Lower.

Willis' extensive description of the visceral nerves and their function is praised by Hierons and Meyer as "certainly more detailed and more accurate than the best accounts before him by Fallopius, Vidius and Vesling." (108) Willis observed that nerves from both vagus and sympathetic trunks invest the arteries and veins "by thickset rows of processes" (e.g. B 24, p. 334), or that they are wound, or strapped around them (Cap. cit., p. 320) in various ways. He concluded that the walls of the vessels receive a constant supply of spirits that enable them "to imitate the movement of the heart," and that, "constricted by this kind of nervous bridles, [they] moderate the course of the blood according to the impulses of the passions, and the instincts" (ibid., p. 334 f). He assumes that one of the tasks of the autonomic nerves consists in dilating and constricting the blood vessels according to the requirements of changing outside conditions in order to achieve a consensus of functions throughout the whole body. (ibid., p. 319 f., 26. Chap., p. 360) He also described a branch of the vagus going to the aortic arch in order to react to changes in the pulse. Sheehan (quoted from (108)) called this "surely the earliest reference to the depressor nerve."

Willis attempted to explore the functions of the vagus by animal experiments: in a dog he ligated both vagus nerves in order to find out whether cardiac pulse depended exclusively from the supply of spirits through the vagi. The dog became at once mute and rigid and "suffered from convulsions about the hypochondria with great trembling of the heart; but after this short attack had ceased, he lay like dying, without any vigour, or sign of life, too lazy or unable to move, and spitting out any food offered: nevertheless its life endured, and was not immediately extinguished even when those nerves had been completely cut in two: but this animal lived on nearly long enough to be killed by weakness from long hunger." When it was dissected the blood in the ventricles and in the great vessels was found "very much coagulated in clotters;" Willis ascribed this to stagnation because of the absence of the accustomed movements in the precordial region deprived of its supply of spirits. (B 24, p. 323 ff.)

MODERN EXPRESSIONS AND CONCEPTS

In "Cerebri Anatome" a word appeared for the first time: νευρολογία, neurology, in the Greek form. Willis called neurology "institutum nostrum" (B 29, p. 422), which means "our project," or, also, "our product" or "creation." To Willis *neurologia* was his description of the peripheral nervous system as distinguished from the central nervous system. He speaks of a general, and of a special neurology. (B 20, p. 273) He is regarded as the founder of neurology by Feindel. (107) "Neurology" has been introduced into the English language through the translation of Willis' works by Pordage. (G, 1681, 1684) (107)

In an epilogue to "Cerebri Anatome" (B, p. 455) Willis promised to write a book about the body-soul, the soul of brutes. This *psychologia* (in Greek) seemed to him a necessary—and more agreeable—completion of the asperities of "Cerebri Anatome," which he compared to a skeleton much in need of the fleshy parts of a science of the soul. Willis fulfilled his promise in 1672; the expression *psychology* was also introduced into English by Pordage's translation. (115, cf. 8)

Willis uses *physiologia* (in Latin script) in the sense it has today: Physiologia de usu partium, physiology as contrast and complement to pathology. (preface and 5. Chap., p. 66) The concept had already been coined by Fernel, but it was not yet generally accepted in Willis' days.

Willis expected to arrive at a "more complete and more accurate physiology of the uses of the parts" (loc. cit.) with the help of comparative anatomy. The expression "anatomia comparata" had been introduced before by Bacon (Cole, 106b), but Bacon meant by it anatomical investigation of many individuals of one species. Willis was the first who understood by this expression the comparison of specific parts in various species of brutes, and in man: "anybody who wants to attribute great importance to names may ascribe the beginning of comparative anatomy . . . to Willis, since he for the first time uses the expression . . ." (Schmidt, 110) Schmidt's history of comparative anatomy begins with "Severino, Willis, Perrault, and Collins." Soury (105a) considers "Cerebri Anatome" a comparative anatomy of the brain. Canguilhem (111a) ascribes this method of Willis to the influence of William Harvey's teachings.—Willis has rightly been called one of the founders of comparative neuroanatomy and of comparative behavior studies. (108)

The word hormones also appears in Greek in "Cerebri Anatome:" τά ὁρμῶντα. Willis gives this name to the animal spirits because they transmit the impulses (in Greek: ὁρμαί, B 14, p. 180). In fact, his concept of animal spirits is very near to our concept of hormones: both are substances "distilled" from the circulating blood which initiate or set in motion (ὁρμάω) a multitude of body reactions.

The concept of reflex action, too, made its first appearance in "Cerebri Anatome." (Canguilhem, 111b) Although Descartes had already described reflexes which he interpreted as automatic processes, it was Willis who first conceived "the thing, the word, and the idea." (Canguilhem, 111c) Sherrington (81b) also writes that the concept of reflex action goes back more clearly to Willis than to Descartes. As results from Canguilhem's book about the formation of this concept, Willis really coined the term and defined its meaning (111d), and the basic notions of the later reflex physiologists generally point to Willis as their founder. (111e)

THE CIRCLE OF WILLIS

Willis thought that the blood vessels of the brain were interconnected everywhere in order to ensure compensation of every deficient vessel by its neighbor. He described the ring of the great arteries at the base of the brain, explaining it as a safety device against possible deficiency of the supplying arteries. He substantiated his opinion by anatomical dye injection, and through the excellent post mortem study of a case of occlusion of one carotid artery without neurological dysfunctions. (B 7, p. 93 ff.; (56, 108)) This circle had been described before with a gradual increase of accuracy (108) ; in 1658 Johann Jakob Wepfer of Schaffhausen had given quite the same details as Willis (108, 113); though Willis, in 1664, published the first illustration of a completed circle, he never claimed priority for this discovery. (108) To judge from their books, and Wepfer's letters, Willis and Wepfer held each other in high esteem. (114, cf. B 1, p. 7) In spite of the historical misconception there seems to be a certain justice in the fact that the circle is now named after Willis, since this eponym is so widely used that at least the name of the man who "put the brain and nervous system on their modern footing" (Sherrington, 118) is still engraved in the brain of every medical graduate.

DEBUNKING WILLIS

Willis wrote in the preface of "Cerebri Anatome" that the book contained the results of his work with Lower, Wren and Millington, and he explicitly stated what each of them contributed. Anthony à Wood, in the article about Lower in his "Athenae Oxonienses" (1), wrote: "Whatsoever is anatomical in that Book, the Glory thereof belongs to the said R. Lower, whose indefatigable Industry at Oxon produced that Elaborate Piece . . . " It was chiefly Michael Foster (44) who elaborated this idea into an audacious theory: he contends that Willis was but a fashionable practioner who contributed hardly more than his name to "Cerebri Anatome," whereas Lower, a real scientist, did most of the research. According to Foster, the worth of the book is far above the worth of its author (meaning Willis). In the same passage Foster has to admit that he found useful physiologic concepts in Willis' other books; but he concludes that Willis must have borrowed these ideas from the "real scientists" he used to meet. In his history of comparative anatomy, Cole (106a) partly follows Foster's theory, but he admits that it is impossible to distinguish the role of the "various members of the society" in formulating the text;

he assumes that this task was "the privilege of their priestly leader" (meaning Willis) . C.C. Mettler goes far beyond that in her version of the theory: she simply calls Willis "something of a dandy,"—while his contemporaries represent him as a man of drab appearance who couldn't even speak fluently. Mettler also says that the important part of his work comes from Lower and Wren.

The opinions of these critics have been rejected by Dow (55), Snow Miller (54), and Symonds (56): it has been proved that the only direct source of their theories, the passage from Wood quoted above, is highly compromised. (See above p. 34) It seem's likely that the combination of epoch-making scientific ideas and discoveries with reckless speculation and overt nonsense which is typical of Willis' books, and the vicarious logical discipline of the successful author were just too much for Foster's logical puritanism. (111f) Possibly a bias of Foster, the physiologist, against Willis, the practitioner, might have been of influence. (56) However, it is quite certain that the debunking theories could never have been conceived, had their authors known Willis' works as a whole. Throughout all his books the same inspired scientific imagination makes its presence felt; the same kind of surprising insights and seemingly easy-won successes appear alongside with the same kind of misconceptions, whereas the team of researchers keeps changing. It is enough to compare Willis' "Of Fevers" with Lower's famous "De Corde" to recognize the fact that Willis was the one whose genius was able to surmount the limitations imposed by the universal lack of information, that only Willis could have been able to correlate the incoherent facts found by the researchers, and that his personal drive must have been the motor force behind the first brain research project in history, whereas Lower was an addict of perfection and steady, well-founded progress. Lower's own words betray the extent to which he was fascinated by his master, and his reluctance to assert a divergent opinion: "I relied more in the matter [of the color of the blood in the pulmonary veins] on the authority and preconceived opinion of the learned Dr. Willis than on my own experience, and confused too far the torch of life with its torch bearer, as, too, the lapse of time has now taught me differently, I shall not be loath to exchange my former view for a better one" (De Corde, 1669, quot. from Fulton, (168)

EVALUATION

Willis has been called the "father of cerebral localization" (H. Boruttau, quoted in (54) and (108)), and "the first inventor of the nervous system" (J. Freind, The History of Physick, quoted in (54)). For Sprengel (76b) and F. H. Garrison (70) "Cerebri Anatome" is the first, most complete, and most accurate treatise of the whole nervous system that had turned up until that time (Sprengel). As quoted above, Sherrington, in

"Man on his Nature" (118) writes that Willis put the brain and nervous system on their modern footing, so far as that could then be done.

Among Willis' attempts at localization, the following statements are the most outstanding: the grey crust, or cortex, generates the agents (spirits) that transmit the impulses, and it is the seat of the memories, while the white matter consists of the minute canals in which those agents travel toward their destination. The cerebellum generates and distributes the spirits that cause the involuntary movements; it governs the autonomic nerves. The corpora striata are the *sensorium commune,* the first sensory center.

Willis' interpretation of the corpora striata as the common sensory center strikes us as farfetched, especially since he actually deduced their importance in voluntary movements from his knowledge of their pathologic antatomy. He thinks that the striata are the place where sensory and sensible impressions from inner and outer organs arrive and modify each other, where first-level perception of these impressions takes place, where they may cause reflexive involuntary local movements such as a scratch-reflex (in man). A very similar concept is still being printed in well-known textbooks of our time, e.g. in Brock and Krieger: "Basis of Clinical Neurology," 1963 (177): "this is the great sensory center. In it, certain vital sensations make conscious registration and are compounded, forming the basis of complicated instinctive reflexes." Of course, not the striatum but the thalamus is thus defined today: an organ far less imposing macroscopically than the grossly structured striopallidum.

The cerebellum is another macroscopically impressive motor structure to which Willis ascribes complex functions belonging to a less imposing part in the neighborhood. Here, too, he succeeds in grasping quite correctly the main pattern of these functions in spite of his shifting their localization. In the case of the cerebellum the error is probably partly due to the crudeness of his experiments: anyone trying to damage or eliminate the cerebellum in Willis' time must have damaged the medulla as well. It is known that later on the defenders of the Willisian localization theory were thus misled by their animal experiments. (117)

In medical history erroneous theories may be regarded as mere curiosities or as suitable examples for the way something should not be done; sometimes, however, they prove to be distinguished steps toward a better understanding: the latter applies to Willis' incorrect localizations. Up to the late eighteenth century defective observation and faulty reasoning led to localization of the main activities of the central nervous system in the ventricles, or in the pineal body, and the like; in Willis' time some physicians still thought that the cerebral and cerebellar hemispheres were essentially the same organs and could replace each other in case of destruction; but Willis contrived to narrow down the extent of error to neighboring brain organs, and to divine quite correctly the nature of the activities of the organs he failed to recognize. These unique feats of intuitive synthesis established once and for all the modern notion of patterns of central nervous activities; but it took one of his very mistakes to set in motion the development of experimental physiology of the central nervous system.

"In the second half of the seventeenth century," writes Neuburger (117a), "an immense revolution in research methods of brain physiology took place, originating from a way of thinking changed by Harvey's discovery, and directly brought about by the localization theory that Willis had formulated in his imperishable work. This theory was the first, which by defining more exactly the connection between the central nervous system and the vital organs led to verifying animal experiments . . . and it opened a new era of brain physiology by ascribing to the cerebellum functions accessible to scientific investigation." Neuburger calls Willis "the ancestor of experimental brain physiology." He speaks of a "Willisian period" of brain research, meaning the period between Willis and Haller in which "the concept of localization was expounded under Willisian influence." (117b)

In other branches of knowledge the Willisian influence reached far beyond the time of Haller. "Cerebri Anatome" was the basis of the successive fundamental investigations of primate brains (e.g. Tyson's chimpanzee of 1699, cf. (106a). In his "History of Materialism" of 1873 (178) F. A. Lange wrote: "Considering the brain in its relation to the mental forces it is especially striking how much the whole argumentation of today's Materialism is similar to that of La Mettrie. . . . La Mettrie (the "ignorant") . . . painstakingly has studied the epoch-making work of Willis about the anatomy of the brain, taking from it everything that serves his purpose. That is why he already knows the significance of the convolutions of the brain, the difference in the relative development of various parts of the brain in higher and lower animals, and so on."

Franz Joseph Gall, the man who in the beginning of the nineteenth century found the language centers (known today as Broca's area) and thus initiated the development of the current doctrines of localization (179), had an ample knowledge of Willis' writings (180); there is every reason to assume that he renewed and transformed a great part of Willis' ideas; he was the first author after Willis to realize the importance of the grey cortex and to make use of the comparison between human psychology and animal behavior.

When Nicolaus Steno, or Niels Stensen, held his famous discourse on the anatomy of the brain one year after Willis' brain anatomy had been published, he said that "The best Figures of the Brain are those of Willis; but even these contain a great number of important Mistakes . . . " Although he acknowledged some of Willis' merits, he finally counted him among *ces affirmateurs,* "these positive gentlemen . . . who prefer the applause of the publick to sincerity and truth." His was a very modern conviction, a kind of positivist scepticism suggestive of attitudes of the late nineteenth and the twentieth century; but his critical review of the brain research of the age, itself partly but an echo of Willis' volley of ideas, did not exert much influence upon later developments, and his positivist convictions finally capsized into mysticism. The time was clearly not for sceptics, at least not in brain research, where only a scientific adventurer like Willis could be expected to overcome the incredible paucity of information.

PATHOLOGIAE CEREBRI ET NERVOSI GENERIS SPECIMEN IN QUO AGITUR DE MORBIS CONVULSIVIS, ET SCORBUTO

This "Specimen of the Pathology of the Brain and Nervous System, in which the Convulsive Diseases and Scurvy are discussed" (C) was published in Oxford in 1667. Willis called his book a specimen because, as he said in the preface, he did not want "to hang these preliminary theories out for sale like a merchant," but wished to expose them to be discussed as examples subject to doubt. In most baroque metaphors he apologized for the lack of perfection and the monstrosity of this *foetus* of his, promising further treatises in which he intended to elaborate upon the same subjects.

"Pathologiae Cerebri . . . " was the first book by

Willis to be reviewed in the "Philosophical Transactions," the journal of the Royal Society that had been founded shortly before.

DE SCORBUTO

Willis thinks that scurvy is the result of a humoral disturbance (dyscrasia) of sal and sulphur in the blood, in the nervous juice, or in both these humors. This disease is discussed in an appendage to the account of the convulsive diseases because Willis believes that scorbutic disturbances in the nervous juice often lead to convulsions. He rightly complains that scurvy in his time serves as a general scapegoat on which those symptoms are heaped which cannot be explained otherwise. Willis intends to reduce this "immense medley of symptoms" to those that really belong to scurvy—but hardly more than a third of the symptoms he finally accepted, could today be explained as effects of ascorbic acid deficiency. What is more, the whole treatise on scurvy is badly arranged and appears to have received but a sketchy finish, perhaps because the author's interest had already been captured by the convulsive diseases. A striking example for this is the account of alimentary influences on scurvy: Willis states that people who eat mainly salt meat and smoked meat, and drink much wine and "burning waters" (aquas ardentes), will get scurvy much more often than people living on dairy products, raw and unripe fruit, and other "absurdities" (absurda); but some pages below he recommends to exclude both kinds of diet from the table of scurvy patients. Throughout his great catalogue of remedies some lucky hits like mild cider, the recommendation of berry wines, decoctions of pine tops have received no further attention by the author; they only go to show that in his gleanings in the lore of empiric and folk medicine he was not guided by credulity alone. Among Willis' writings, "De Scorbuto" stands out as a neglected by-product, lacking that groundwork of theories which, throughout Willis' written work, connects his observations and knowledge into meaningful patterns.

DE MORBIS CONVULSIVIS

Willis puts among the convulsive diseases a wide variety of affections ranging from epilepsy through the convulsive diseases of children, convulsive states originating from the roots, the plexus, the processes of the nerves, from disorders of the nervous juice, and from scorbutic disposition, to hysteria, convulsive cough, and asthma. In all these diseases, according to Willis, the convulsions, or spasms occurring in the sceletal muscles, in the visceral parts, or in the spirits of the brain are the leading characteristics.

As Temkin (125) says, Willis was the first author

who elaborated these ideas into a useful system. He succeeded in separating atypical affections from what was then regarded as epilepsy in a strict sense, and he made it possible to apply the term to a clearly defined disease.

Apart from his hypotheses on the spirits and their explosion, the chief source of the pathogenetic theories in this book was the theory of Charles Le Pois, or Piso, who had nearly identified epilepsy and hysteria, explaining both as diseases of the brain, though he employed extremely simplified mechanistic concepts. (125, 126)

BASIC CONCEPTS

Before we can come to a better understanding of the nature and causes of convulsive movements, Willis says, we must be able to explain the nature and causes of movement.—The following account contains supplementary information from "Cerebri Anatome," (B 19, 238 ff) .—In the nervous juice, contained in the pores of the nerves which can be seen through the microscope, the animal spirits are moving about. By their movements they are transmitting sensory impressions and motor impulses. These movements, because of their immense velocity, can better be compared to the emanation of light rays than to the flow of liquids. The inflowing (influi) spirits that reach the motor parts travelling through the nerves, may be compared to the particles of the light rays, whereas the insitting (insiti) spirits that stay in those parts are similar to the particles in the air that upon activation by the light rays generate the diffuse, indirect light. These latter spirits are also compared to still waters that may be put in motion by flowing waters.

These local, or insitting spirits in the muscle are produced by the extremities of the nerve fibres (but sometimes Willis also remarks that they come from tendinous fibres in the muscle). They are the immediate instruments of muscular movement: their spirituo-saline particles go into compounds with the nitro-sulphureous particles from arterial blood which act as *copula elastica,* that is, make the compound elastic, or enable it to expand. This compound is then ignited, as it were, by the instinct of movement that reaches the muscle through the animal spirits in the nerve, and when ignited, it explodes like gunpowder. By the explosion the muscle is inflated, and consequently shortened. The copula elastica is supplied in any amounts, and forever renewed, by the arterial blood, whereas the supply of spirits is not so liberal because the nerves are much thinner than the arteries. But the spirits endure for a long time: they are able to go into new compounds after a copula elastica has been spent in an explosion. (C 1, 1-2)

Willis attempts to substantiate his explosion theory by comparing it to various chemical reactions known to be extremely violent, as, for instance, the reactions between mineral acids and metals. He quotes Gassendi who writes that the anima ignea, the fiery soul (corresponding to Willis' anima corporea, or soul of brutes) has virtually the same effect in the body as the small flame out of gunpowder has in war, where it drives asunder the cannonball and the heavy gun.

This theory of nervous and muscular action is of central importance in Willis' work since it is the elementary basis of his physiology and pathology of the whole nervous system, and the basis of the psychology and psychopathology he developed in his four books on the nervous system. (B, C, D, E) It is also the main connection between Willis' iatrochemistry and his views about the nervous system.

By animal spirit Willis understands basically a chemical principle. This is consistent with a trend of his time in which, as Sherrington (118) writes, "the spirits of the life-soul were tending, literally, to 'materialize.' Only a century before they, in the microcosm of the body, had been the counterpart of the celestial ether in the macrocosm, the universe." As we have seen above (p. 49), the latter idea is still inherent in Willis' concept of spirit as an elementary principle, but at the same time, in another direction, his ideas go far beyond a mere materialistic explanation of animal spirit.

It is quite astonishing that the fact that "under the same traditional name of animal spirits, Willis conceives an idea of the thing which is nearly without precedent" (Canguilhem, 111b) has escaped the notice of most historians in the field. "Because Willis conceives the double movement of centripetal and centrifugal propagation of the animal spirits not only in the image of light as did van Helmont, but in the images of every phenomenon susceptible to inversion by reflexion, in the image of the waves on the surface of the water as well as in the image of sound and echo" (loc. cit.). This is the new concept of the animal spirit as a material agent which, in the living body, cannot be defined by its material properties alone, but is characterized, as it were, by its movement, its potency for transmission and detonation, and by the hypothetical localization of its varying effects. The idea of the way of acting of this spirit, "the intellectual constant of an astonishing variety of expressions and metaphors," (loc. cit.) proved a highly useful contrivance that led Willis directly towards the development of the concept or reflex action. (cf. 111b) Canguilhem (111) who has succeeded in elucidating most of the history of these ideas has shown that some of Willis' metaphors are still being used in physiology textbooks of the twentieth century; he also quotes a passage from Bergson where a great number of Willisian analogies, including that of explosion causing muscular movement, are taken up again. Vinchon and Vie (122) write that Willis' concept of nerve action, brought forward in an epoch in which electricity was unknown, approximated the animal spirits to our nerve current (influx nerveux); and Willis, in fact, used the same word for the supply of spirits to the nerve: "novo semper influxu. . . ." (B, 19, 238) A minority of writers has become aware of the prophetic character (J. Lhermitte, 123) of these theories "of the explosion of the animal spirits, or as we would put it, of nervous discharge . . . " (Soury, 105d); Canguilhem thinks that "Willis' dynamic theory is a vague and distant foreboding of the energetic way of thought" (111b); but even these well-informed authors did not take into consideration the obvious tendency toward kinetic and energetic explanations of natural phenomena that marks Willis' very first work, the "De Fermentatione." (AA) In fact, Willis' interpretation of fermentation as the result of a struggle between the innate forces of divers kinds of particles may already be called energetic (cf. Oppenheimer, 121) : and it is from these explicative comparisons, not from Helmontian concepts, that he arrives at his revolutionary ideas on nerve action.

From his explanation of regular movements Willis goes on to account for the convulsive movements, or convolutions, or spasms, as distinguished from tetanic contractions into which he does not inquire any further. He thinks that only seldom convulsions will arise from obvious causes alone (e.g. from local irritation by means of reflex action): convulsions of any considerable violence, persistence, and frequency result, in all probability, from alien particles of great explosivity, which are compounded with the animal spirits instead of the copula elastica. These particles are called copula explosiva. They are the underlying cause, the procatarxis, of most convulsive diseases.

It is through defects both in the brain and in the

blood that the explosive particles are enabled to pass from the blood into the brain. The blood can supply such particles to the brain if it is changed by a disease, or if it is charged with particles of noxious ferments originating from abscesses, venomous ulcers, or diseases of inner organs. These particles are admitted only if the brain's constitution is already weakened, because in its normal state its narrow pores will admit only the appropriate spirituous humor (the nervous juice with the animal spirits). If the pores relax too much, or if the spirits guarding them fail in their duty, inappropriate material may get into the brain. Bad constitution of the brain may be inherited, or acquired after birth. The brain may be either too humid, or too dry, or its pores may be too lax, its consistency too hard, or too soft, or the shape of some of its parts may be extraordinary; the brain may be weakened by accidents, bad habits or ways of life, severe or chronical diseases; extreme heat or cold, or wounds often disturb the balance of its humors, and render it susceptible to alien matter.

If explosive particles get into the brain, they may still be drained away through the veins and lymphatic vessels without doing much damage. If some such particles go into compounds with the spirits in the brain for a short time, they cause only visual disturbances and vertigo. Even if they cannot be drained away at once, they do not cause great damage, since in the spacious brain the spirits can get away from them instead of forming compounds, which would not be possible in the narrow nerve canals. If the explosive particles cannot be evacuated through the vessels, they are soon dismissed into the dependent parts (the nervous system). If they stay in the brain for a longer time, which does not occur very often, they cause epilepsy. (C1, 5-7)

Explosive particles that reach the nervous system are distributed according to certain rules. Thus, in children the nerves of the face which are situated most closely to the brain are attacked before the others, in adults, vagus, intercostalis (sympathicus) and spinal cord are often seized, whereas in patients of weak constitutions the praecordia and entrails are most often affected.

The animal spirits that are compounded with explosive particles usually dwell in the nerves, especially in the plexus. Crowding or irritation compels them to drive out their explosive particles which then inflate the dependent parts and cause movements contrary to the commands of nature or will. The spirits thus incited into convulsive movements carry along their neighbors, so that convulsions spread from the limbs to the brain, and vice versa.

Among the so-called evident or obvious causes there are many that may trigger the action of the copula explosiva. Violent passions, like fright, anger, grief, suddenly irritate the spirits, and irritations of the entrails can cause convulsions not necessarily restricted to the vicinity, since, by reflex action, convulsions in distant parts may be incited by them. Whenever convulsions apparently coming from such causes are severe, one must search for an underlying cause: a copula explosiva.

EPILEPSY

This is the most important among the convulsive diseases, because it seizes the brain and every part of the nervous system with great power. A well-known English theologist thinks that many of the possessed in the New Testament were but epileptics, and that the healing of this disease by the Saviour has subsequently been called exorcism of an evil spirit. It is a fact that traces of the morbific matter can hardly ever be found in this disease, so that it may be feasible to suppose the influence of an evil spirit. However it is quite probable that the Devil himself, if he be allowed to torment mortals, could not find a more effective means to do it than through attacks of this monstrous disease.

Willis supposes that the epileptic fit (which, like the prodromes and the aura, he correctly describes in detail) results from a sudden explosion of the spirits in the brain which causes loss of consciousness and sets off convulsions in the nerves. His hypothesis enables him to explain the sudden onset and breaking off of the seizures, and the lack of traces of a morbific matter. The morbific matter does not reach the solid parts since it is compounded with the spirits. The primary seat of the disease is always the center of the brain, where the animal spirits that perform the activities of the inner sense—of imagination and striving, or appetite—are compounded with the copula explosiva, and then explode. In severe seizures the copula explosiva can invade the rest of the brain and the whole nervous system, and the original explosion then spreads quite like an explosion in scattered gunpowder: the initial loss of consciousness is followed by convulsions in every part of the body. (C 2)

Willis distinguishes primary from secondary epilepsy: the brain is seized either in the first place, or secondarily, by consensus. In secondary epilepsy the seizure seems to start from a finger, a toe, or an internal part, ascending quickly towards the head, accompanied by sensations of pins and needles, or by a cold aura. The epileptic then falls to the ground, loses consciousness, and is subject to further typical symptoms. In these cases the cause of epilepsy is generally believed to dwell in the part first attacked and to influence the brain from there. But Willis affirms that the cause of every kind of epilepsy is always in the brain, where the spirits associated with a copula explosiva bring about the symptoms of primary as well as of secondary epileptic fits. Peripheral initial symptoms as described above are very rarely evident causes: in most cases they are simply precursory phenomena. The Willisian theory of nerve action allows for an explanation of this concept of Le Pois: if the spirits in the center of the brain and in the medulla are so saturated with explosive particles that they are ready to explode, and to initiate a fit, the spirits in the more distant parts can get out of order because the accustomed supply of spirits from the brain fails to arrive, and this disturbance can cause convulsions that wander from the nerve endings towards the brain where they act like a fuse detonating the predisposed spirits.

Epilepsy is also differentiated according to various other characteristics. It is either inherited or acquired, it occurs before, or after, puberty, the afflicted patients lose consciousness, or retain it. It can also be differentiated according to the temperaments, and to many other points.

The foam at the mouth of the epileptic is generally explained as an effect of the compression of the brain by which a liquid would be squeezed into the oral cavity; but anatomy has shown no possible passage for such a liquid from the brain to the mouth. Willis thinks that the foaming saliva results from convulsions of the nerves which command the movements of the lungs and diaphragm: the lungs and precordia being forcibly lifted, air, viscous fluid, and white of egg (ovi albumen) are mixed and stirred and driven out into the oral cavity by the frequent irregular movements of these parts. For the same reason many epileptics will beat their chests during seizures; the precordia are constricted by convulsions, the blood stagnates, the heart is oppressed, life itself is threatened with suffocation—and the afflicted patients, whose brain is not conscious of the act (cerebro inscio), try to regain the regular movements by mere natural instinct (mero naturae instinctu). A similar act occurs when sleepers tickled or bit by a flea unconsciously (inscii) scratch the irritated spot.

Epilepsy is very difficult to cure because the center of the brain does not only suffer from the effects of the morbific matter, but also from the fits themselves, which make it weak, and more readily accessible for alien matter. But still, the disease may spontaneously come to an end: this happens almost exclusively during puberty, since in that period the explosive particles are not only deposited in the brain, but also in the spermatic glands, so that the brain is less heavily beset by them; and in that period the blood receives a ferment from the gonads consisting of particles imbued with seminal tincture by which the blood is strengthened and stimulated. This same ferment also incites the nervous juice into a new fermentation. If the ferments that cause epilepsy are not overpowered by this new ferment, they often cannot be defeated until death. (C 3, 16)

Epilepsy most often attacks children and adolescents. If a person has had a seizure and is not cured by remedies, or by the onset of puberty, he will hardly ever get free of the disease. The greater the frequency of the fits, the more severe they become; if they recur very often, they weaken memory, imagination, and reason, and finally the totality of the animal functions (i.e. of the functions of the nervous system) is impaired. Towards the end the vital activitics, that is, the functions of the heart, the lung, the intestines, slowly perish. (C 2) The disease can be fatal, but it may also turn into another disease like a palsy, idiocy, or a melancholy that is mostly incurable.

The prescriptions of the dogmatics who try to drive out the morbific matter nearly exclusively through evacuating agents are useless, and often harmful, in the treatment of epilepsy. Exclusive use of empiric remedies may sometimes bring about a cure, but the cure is far more certain if the body has been prepared for empiric treatment according to the rules of the art of medicine. Epilepsy can be treated in a curative, or in a prophylactic way: curative through suppression of beginning seizures, prophylactic through evacuation of the morbific matter.—During attacks vomitives and purges should be avoided, and bleeding should be used with restraint. In long-lasting unconsciousness enemas are very useful. — The first objective must be fixation of the all too volatile spirits; their explosions must be suppressed. Medicaments capable of fixing the spirits contain volatile salts, ammonia, or vitriolic sulphur: these are succinic salt and succinic oil, spirit of blood and of hartshorn, spirit of soot, and castorean tincture. The spirits can be kept from exploding by being attracted to, and occupied with their accustomed activities; therefore prolonged frictions of the whole body often help to suppress an impending seizure. During seizures, many physicians have the epileptics held by force, or even more roughly mistreated: but they only double their torments, and it would be much better to let the attacks take their own course.

In spite of his acid comment upon dogmatic practice, Willis says that prophylactic treatment consisting in the evacuation of the cause of the disease is the most effective method. It takes the morbific matter out of the blood, the nervous juice and the entrails, and it improves the bad disposition of the brain and its spirits. For this evacuation vomitives, purgatives, bleeding and other purifying agents are used. Though it is nearly impossible to cure epilepsy by these methods alone, by their effects the obstacles of treatment are eliminated, and Nature is enabled to attack its enemy itself. Subsequently the specific remedies are administered, such as peony, mistletoe, rue, castor, elk's claw, preparations from human skulls, from amber, from coral, and many others. The way these empiric remedies act, is not clear; it is possible that they strengthen the brain and constrict its pores, barring the entrance to the copula explosiva. At least the general astringent properties of peony, mistletoe, rue and many others of these substances are quite obvious.

HYSTERIA AND HYPOCHONDRIA

"The hysterical passion is of so ill fame among the Diseases belonging to Women, that like one half damn'd, it bears the faults of many other Distempers: For when at any time a sickness happens in a Womans Body, of an unusual manner, or more occult original, so that its cause lies hid, and the curatory indication is altogether uncertain, presently we accuse the evil influence of the Womb (which for the most part is innocent) and in every unusual symptom, we declare it to be something Hysterical, and so to this scope, which oftentimes is only the subterfuge of ignorance, the medical intentions and use of Remedies are directed." (C 10, quoted from G)

The symptoms most often found are these: movements in the lower abdomen, something like a globe ascending in the belly, murmurs in the intestines, a tendency to vomit, inflation of the hypochondria with growlings and hiccough, unequal, and usually obstructed breathing, a sensation of choking in the throat, dizziness, rolling and coruscation of the eyes, frequent laughing and crying, absurd confabulations, sometimes loss of voice and movement with hardly detectable or failing pulse and deathlike aspect, sometimes convulsions in the face, in the limbs, or, in severe cases, in the whole body. The tragedy of the hysteric seizure is staged mostly in the adomen, in the chest, or in the head, or subsequently in these parts (paroxysmi tragoedia peragitur). (C 10, 69) The disease occurs in women of every age and station, including the ages before puberty and after the climacteric, and sometimes also in men.

Most ancient, and some modern (neoterici) doctors believe that the disease is caused by an ascension of the womb, or by vapours arising from it. Willis objects that in virgins and widows the womb is so small and so firmly attached to the surrounding parts that it could not move from its place and ascend, nor could its movements be felt, if there were any. Moreover, a descensus or prolapse of the womb, though seen quite often, rarely or never causes hysteria, whereas the displacements of the womb toward one side which often occur in childbed do not result in hysteria at all. Still, the womb may occasionally become a starting-point of convulsions, like all other entrails, since local convulsions may result from an organic lesion (solutio continui) of these parts, and such local convulsions may dispose the brain to convulsions through consensus or conveyance by the nerves. A general convulsive disposition can also be caused by stagnation of the nervous juice when evacuation of menstrual blood, female spermatic fluid, or leucorrhoea is obstructed.

The womb has been defended against the traditional accusations by LePois and Highmore. Highmore ascribes the hysterical symptoms to an overflow of blood in the pneumonic vessels. Nearly apologizing, Willis says that he is compelled to refute this opinion lest his own theory be discredited by it. He contends that hysterical seizures often begin without any respiratory symptoms, that they may take their course completely without any respiratory disorders, and that an overflow of blood in the pnuemonic vessels as postulated by Highmore must necessarily cause extravasation, inflammation, and peripneumonia, whereas according to Highmore the attack caused by it ought to be a quickly passing dysfunction. Moreover anemic women are especially prone to attacks of hysteria: in anemic states such a plethora in the lungs is entirely unthinkable.

Willis is convinced that "the so-called Uterine affection is chiefly, and in the first place convulsive, and that it most probably depends from an affected brain and nervous system. . . . " (C 10, 70) He thinks that this doctrine allows for the best explanation of the startling and incoherent diversity of symptoms. The disease often begins shortly after sudden fright, immense sadness, indignation, or any other violent passion: these affective changes disturb the spirits in the brain and in the cranial nerve roots and render them susceptible to alien particles so that they easily compound with a copula explosiva. It has been demonstrated that the spirits meet the explosive particles mostly in the roots of the cranial nerves because noxious juices use to gather there. (This is a description of the famous *colluvies serosa* or serous confluence at the cranial nerve roots which Le Pois had found in postmortems, believing it to be the common mechanical cause of epilepsy and hysteria (cf. 126)). The course of the seizures also points to a mechanism of this kind, since they often begin with a sensation of fullness in the head, vertigo, coruscation of the eyes, and buzzing in the ears: "The reason why such a copula, adhering to the spirits, is most probably conveyed . . . into the interior nerves is that in these passages towards the praecordia and entrails the spirits are more easily disturbed by the passions *(animi affectus)*: therefore they more readily accept noxious matter introduced from elsewhere, and more quickly conceive anomalies." (C 10, 71) Though in another terminology, and according to his own views, Willis says here clearly that hysterical symptoms will develop most often in the realms of the autonomic nervous system because the autonomic nervous system is more susceptible to affective disorders than any other part of the body.

Hypochondria, Willis says, is also a convulsive disease. Its symptoms are partly those of hysteria, but the most characteristic are disorders of the stomach and heart, timidity leading to suspicion of everything, imaginary diseases, and unrest of thought. Women will less frequently suffer from hypochondria than men, since in women, because of their weaker constitution, the obviously convulsive symptoms are more prevalent than in men. It is said that in the female sex the hysterical is added to the hypochondriacal affection. Hypochondria has been generally ascribed to the spleen, and to vapors arising from it. Willis explains it as a convulsive disease that acts through the nervous system, but nevertheless he attempts to connect this nervous disturbance to the spleen: he thinks that the spleen acts upon the blood by means of its ferment, and upon the nervous system by consensus, in both ways influencing the brain which then causes the disease. Willis again refutes a theory of Highmore who thinks that hypochondria is caused by the stomach.

Willis' therapy of the hysterical (C 10, 78-80) and the hypochondriacal (C 11, 87-89) affections is quite complex. He thinks that light hysterical attacks should not be treated. If it becomes necessary "to come to the aid of nature severely oppressed" (naturae valde oppressae suppetias afferre opus sit), general custom may be followed by holding under the patient's nose such strong-smelling substances as asa foetida, or scorched old leatherwork. These substances may also be given internally as solutions. If the attack goes on for some time, or if it results in loss of voice and movement, enemas with stronger substances, frictions of the legs and feet, cupping-glasses, or sternutatories may be administered—or a simple draught of cold water may be given. Long-time treatment begins, as usual, with evacuation in order to eliminate morbific matter and other obstacles of treatment, by vomitories, bleeding, leeches, purgatives, vesicatories and fontanels at the head (small burns exuding serum). The next step is the tuning up or reduction to due consistency (ad crasin debitam reductio) of the blood, which can be obtained by means of iron preparations, mineral waters, butter milk, the use of spas (thermarum usus); even tea and coffee are of some help. Finally the brain and the spirits must be strengthened: this can be done by the same empiric anticonvulsives used against epilepsy. Furthermore, in hypochondria the stomach must be strengthened by digestives, the spleen must be rid of disorders by local external applications, while in hysteria, if there be any signs of organic disorders of the womb, these have to be treated adequately in order to eliminate possible sources of morbific matter.

Willis discusses at length the uses and advantages of

iron or steel preparations, which he calls chalybeata (ibid. p. 79, 88, 89-91) They are made from fine iron filings or iron solutions.

Willis uses them widely as tonics. He warmly recommends their use for anemic patients: " . . . for it is so observed in many affected with the Dropsy, arising from white Phlegm, the Pica or evil longings, or green-sickness, to have a pale countenance, cold blood and waterish; but by the use of steel, the countenance soon to be more florid, and the blood to be imbued with a more intensive tincture and heat. . . . " (C 10, quoted from G) In these cases iron is truly a masterful remedy, but if the blood ferments exceedingly, and effervesces in the hypochondria, that is, if moderate remedies are needed to settle the excess of fermentation, then iron preparations must be avoided.

THE DISPUTE WITH HIGHMORE

Willis had rejected Nathaniel Highmore's doctrine of the origins of hysteria and hypochondria, published in 1660. (127 a) This led to a controversy with Highmore, first (according to Dewhurst, 181) in private correspondence, later published as a reply upon Willis' account of hysteria by Highmore, and a rejoinder by Willis. In the first discussion of Highmore's views in 1667 Willis had expressed his reluctance to antagonize the esteemed and learned Oxford anatomist, the friend of William Harvey; and the whole dispute never ran to those personal invectives and vulgarities that characterize the majority of the learned controversies of the period.

Highmore's "De Hysterica et Hypochondriaca Passione Responsio Epistolaris ad Doctissimum Willisium" (127 b) was published in London in 1670, and reviewed in the "Transactions" of the Royal Society. (124 b) He wrote that hysteria was not always associated with convulsions, that the existence of a nervous juice was doubtful, and that the explosion theory was untenable because Willis could not explain why his proposed explosions should go off only in the muscles and nerves, and never in the blood though all the substances involved were also present there. He then proceeded to defend his theories of an overabundance of blood in the lungs and precordia causing hysteria, and the laxity of the gastric fibres causing hypochondria.

Willis' duply (D) was entitled "Affectionum Quae dicuntur, Hystericae et Hypochondriacae Pathologia Spasmodica Vindicata. Ad Virum Doctissimum Nathanael Highmorum, M.D. Cui accesserunt Exercitationes Medico-Physicae Duae. I. De Sanguinis Accensione. II. De Motu Musculari." It was published in London in 1670, only some months after Highmore's treatise; it was also reviewed in the "Transactions" (124 c), and reprinted in Leiden in 1671. Willis took the trouble of refuting Highmore's arguments with the help of anatomy, pathologic anatomy, chemistry, and bedside observations. The Latin style of the treatise is less ornate and more fluent that that of Willis' other works, and it is strikingly superior to Highmore's barrel-organ drone (cf. 126) : this advantage might have contributed to the success of the Willisian doctrine.

Willis' reply contains some additional information on hysteria and hypochondria, but it is certainly a less important part of Willis' writings than the two short tracts appended to it: "Of the accension of the blood," and "of muscular movement," both of which will be discussed following our remarks about the concepts of neurosis.

SYDENHAM ON HYSTERIA

The second part of Thomas Sydenham's "Epistolary Dissertation to Dr. William Cole" of 1682 is generally regarded as that century's classical description of hysteria. Sydenham explains hysteria as a disorder of the animal spirits, "whereas, as a true believer in the Hippocratic tradition, he ascribes all other diseases to the humors . . ." (Ackerknecht, 128) To Sydenham an *ataxia* of the spirits is the underlying cause of the hysterical symptoms. Willis had often used this expression (written in Greek by both authors) with the same meaning: a disturbance of the natural order of the animal spirits. Because of this *ataxia*, Sydenham writes, the spirits are gathered too tightly in some parts of the body, while other parts are deserted by them, so that their functions are impaired. If the conglomerated (conglomerati) (131 a) spirits invade susceptible parts they cause convulsions and pain. (cf. 131b) Sydenham explains many leading symptoms in terms of convulsions caused by disturbed spirits. (131: pp. 103, 105, 119, 121f., 123, 126) He thus makes use of integrant parts of that theory which Willis had elaborated into a system. Sydenham tells us that the animal spirits "constitute the supreme grade in the scale of matter" and that they are "placed in the very confines of the Immaterial Being"—a notion which had been defined more clearly many years before in Willis' "Of Fermentation." Sydenham also uses the comparison of light rays which had been previously elaborated by Willis: the strictly circumscript headache of hysteric patients, the *clavus hystericus,* or hysteric nail, results from a concentration of spirits from the entire body into one point of the head (Pericranii quasi punctulo concentrantur), a process that is "not very far from that gathering of the Sun's rays that is produced by the burning-glass." (131c)

In Willis' writings the animal spirits are basically identified with a chemically demonstrable substance, and their proposed ways of action are a reasonable complement of the results of anatomical and clinical research into the properties of the nervous system. But Sydenham's animal spirits are completely devoid of any connection to given quantities. Sydenham's spirits are described as the material basis of the mind; theirs are vital tasks in the body which, however, cannot be pinned down in detail; they constitute a system of their own, of which Sydenham has not much to say except that it can be interrupted by any trifle, if its *crasis* or humoral constitution is weak: such interruptions result in the said *ataxia* which in turn causes the hysterical symptoms.

"In the same way as Exterior Man appears to be combined from parts obvious to the senses, there is without doubt also some Interior Man, consisting of the due order, and, as it were, texture of the spirits, and visible only to the light of Reason." (131d) Sydenham takes no trouble to deduct his concepts of the spirits and their disorders from somewhere, to explain, to substantiate, or to justify them: he avoids mentioning any anatomical localization of their activities. He restricts himself to proclaiming the hysterical symptoms as results of disorders of the spirits, and he comes to this conclusion without furnishing any proof beyond expressions like "it is clearer than light," "and it must not be doubted," "Satis itaque iam constat opinor, omnem hunc morbum ad Spiritus Animales non rite dispositos referri debere. . . . " (131e) Sydenham's concepts of animal spirits are so fragmentary, and so completely detached from every possible point of reference, that they cannot be accepted as an autochthonous system; the fact that every idea employed in these conceptions is contained, in more meaningful connections, in the earlier writings of Willis disproves their originality. These distinctly Willisian ideas appear in Sydenham's work without any organic or anatomical references, but this only proves Sydenham's truly Hippocratic way of thinking: on principle he refuses to admit that the patient must be taken to pieces and disjoined into functions and properties of individual organs in order to be understood. (cf. Temkin, 129)

There are further parallels to Willis in Sydenham's treatise on hysteria. Sydenham sometimes uses the same words to describe the same unspecific circumstances as Willis did: hysterical cough to Sydenham is "species . . . oppido rara" (131f), and to Willis "casus . . . oppido rari." (DA, p. 11) The striking similarity of most of the therapy both authors recommend might be explained away with reasons like the common tradition, the medical milieu they both shared, and the like. But both authors write that iron therapy is most important, discussing it at length, and both try to substantiate this claim by describing the effect of iron remedies upon the blood of the anemic (cf. above p. 133). Anyhow, Sydenham's famous boast that he learned his therapy more from his own experience than from reading books (131g), cannot be upheld by the available evidence. It is true that Sydenham's account of hysterical disorders is more lucidly arranged, simpler, and easier to understand than that of Willis. To Willis the description of diseases is the necessary background for his theories, to Sydenham it is the objective of his work. What Sydenham discusses in one short treatise is dispersed over more than a hundred pages of two of

Willis' books. Sydenham attempts "to express in the terminology of his time . . . , that to him the disease is neither purely somatic nor purely psychic." (Ackerknecht, 128) But this had been done long before by Willis, who had been able to find an explanation for the peculiar character of most hysterical symptoms through his concept of the vegetative nervous system that acts as the carrier of the emotions in the body. In view of this fact Sydenham's rather vague secondary attempt at an explanation cannot be judged a contribution to progress.

Except for his statement that hysteria also occurs in men—which also had been said before by Willis—Sydenham does not bother to explain why he has left the traditional belief that hysteria is caused by the womb. We may assume that at the time Sydenham's treatise was published, about ten years after the controversy with Highmore, the Willisian doctrine of hysteria was so well known in England that it was enough to adopt part of its theoretical basis—such as the concept of disorders of the animal spirits—in order to prevail against the adherents of the uterine tradition. This assumption is corroborated by John Ward (132) who, at about the same time, wrote in his diary that most doctors, especially in Oxford, held the same views as Willis and Sydenham. We must conclude from the available evidence that Sydenham relied heavily upon Willis when he wrote about hysteria. We have shown that he also relied on Willis when he wrote about fevers. This seems somewhat paradox since Sydenham certainly had a distaste for medical literature. However, Willis' book about fevers, and his book about convulsive diseases had got a special kind of publicity through the controversies caused by them: such a publicity was sure to reach even the less literate among the London physicians.

TOWARDS THE CONCEPT OF NEUROTIC DISEASE

The development of opinions on hysteria has been described by Glafira Abricossoff in 1897. (126) Her conclusions confirm our results from a survey of general medical history: Le Pois and after him Willis were the first known authors who clearly explained hysteria as a disease of the nervous system. Le Pois' theory was not widely accepted, whereas Willis' theory, says Abricossoff, was defended by Sydenham; the general tendency of these three authors was later taken up by Boerhaave. As the animal spirits had been the acknowledged active principle of the nervous system for about two thousand years, Sydenham's theory must have been mistaken for a nerve theory by a vast majority of his readers; from this point of view his account of hysteria indeed appears to be a simplified version of that of Willis.

Ackerknecht (128) writes that neuroses were studied with special intensity in the seventeenth century, partly "because at that time neurology made its first appearance on the scene." Willis' contribution to neurology was so important that he has been celebrated as its founder (cf. above p. 101f. (106, 107, 108, 111, 112, 116, 118)) It was Willis who succeeded in replacing the crudely mechanistic hypotheses of Le Pois by a theoretical substructure belonging to a comprehensive system that was to be modern for several generations. He was the first who managed to find a plausible connection between the emotional factors and the leading symptoms of hysteria. He also grasped the peculiarly dramatic character of hysterical fits (cf. above p. 128) . His work on hysteria and hypochondria was one of the most decisive steps towards a psychodynamic interpretation of neurotic disease, and towards the shaping of this concept; the ensuing development that brought the disease into the hands of the neurologists is mainly due to the impact of his ideas. But in spite of Le Pois, Willis, Sydenham, and Boerhaave, hysteria was not generally accepted as a nervous disease until the end of the nineteenth century: the neurologist who achieved the next great step, Sigmund Freud, still had to defend his views against the ancient belief of the womb as the cause of hysteria.

THE "TWO MEDICO-PHYSICAL EXERCITATIONS" OF 1670

The two short treatises that were published along with Willis' reply against Highmore had nearly nothing to do with hysteria. As Willis wrote (DB), they already belonged to the theme of his next book, the "Soul of Brutes." Before publishing this psychology of his—a project that certainly was very dear to him since he kept announcing it in his books since 1664—he obviously wanted to modernize some of the underlying theories. In these two treatises he attempts to adjust his hypotheses on metabolism and muscular movement to the recent results of two eminent sceptical scientists, Boyle and Steno.

DE SANGUINIS INCALESCENTIA

The less perfect animals have no warm blood; their organs are so primitive that the meagre supply of the necessary substances from cold blood is sufficient for their needs; in spite of the absence of warmth their blood is perpetually reactivated by its circulation and fermentation. In the more perfect animals the blood must be warm in order to be able always to supply the vital substances to the organs in sufficient quantity. This vital warmth cannot be explained as heat brought into the body from outside, nor is it a result of fermentation. In "Of Fevers" Willis actually thought fermentation was the cause; now he writes that this warmth cannot result from fermentation, though he maintains that fermentation can produce diseases.

Willis judges that "life itself is some kind of flame"

(vitam ipsam flammae speciem quandam esse DB) in the first place because combustion is the only heat-producing process known to him that cannot take place without an adequate supply of air. Every flame on earth consists of sulphureous particles, and of nitrous ones—abounding everywhere in the air—which meets them. Robert Boyle's experiments with his air-pump have shown that flames will suffocate much more rapidly from want of air than from the accumulation of combustion residues in the air. Boyle has also demonstrated that warm-blooded animals perish sooner in his glass sphere if the air is pumped away than if the container is simply closed.

Like any flame, the blood continuously needs fresh sulphureous nutriment (pabulum sulphureum); this is supplied by the digestive parts. Like any flame, the blood must be continuously cleared of its sooty residues, effluvia fuliginosa) by ventilation: this purpose is served by the windpipe and the pores of the skin.

The change of color that has been found in the blood results from its mixture with nitrous air (aeris nitrosi cum sanguine admixtio). Therefore, as Dr. Lower has observed, its color is a blackish purple in the pulmonary arteries, a bright red in the pulmonary veins: it comes into contact with the nitrous air in the lungs. The same bright red color always results at the surface of blood taken from a vein, because at the surface the blood encounters its nitrous nutriment (pabulum nitrosum): if fresh blood is stirred vigorously it will turn bright red all through for the same reason.

Willis assumes that blood warmth comes from a kind of combustion that has every property of fire, or flame, except for the visible shape (species) ; a combustion that neither destroys nor shines, but serves the purposes of life.

It is not the entire blood that takes part in this combustion: in the first place the sulphureous components are consumed this way, whereas the subtler particles are refined into animal spirits, the coarser ones (according to AB, AC, and B, cf. above p. 78f.: something like white of eggs) serve the nutrition and growth of the solid parts of the body, and the residues of spent substances must be evacuated through appropriate organs of excretion. The combustion in the blood is not of the same intensity in every man, and the disposition of the entire soul can depend from the quantity and quality of the vital flame.

Willis' "sulphur" and "sulphureous" is not identical with the substance that bears this name today. According to his descriptions and remarks, this chymical principle is an oily fraction appearing in distillation of most mixed bodies; the combustibility of all kinds of bodies depends on its prevalence; this fraction must have consisted mostly of hydrocarbons. Therefore Willis' concepts of metabolism were largely those described by Liebig as late as 1842. (cf. above p. 79)

Patterson (45) has proved that in this treatise Willis anticipated a great part of what used to be celebrated as John Mayow's great discovery. But Partington (60) succeeded in further elucidating the circumstances of this early discovery of oxygen (which was given names like pabulum nitrosum, nitrosae aeris particula, spiritus nitro-aereus). Instead of a sudden discovery, a slowly advancing development of ideas appears to have taken place in the *philosophical* circles of London and Oxford; and the contributions of George Ent, Ralph Bathurst, Malachi Thruston, and Robert Hooke apparently were as instrumental to this development as those of Boyle, Willis, Lower, and Mayow. Willis was quite closely connected with most of these researchers. George Ent's book of 1641, in which he points out a "nitrous virtue" (virtus nitrosa) as the basis of respiration (60u) is quoted in Willis' "Soul of Brutes" (E, I, 2, p. 6); Ralph Bathhurst who collected the main points of a theory comparing respiration to combustion in his Oxford lectures of 1654 (published in 1761 (60v)) was a personal friend of Willis (cf. above p. 28); Hooke, who took part in the development of the theory, and in its substantiation by experiments, was Willis' assistant and protégé (cf. above p. 22), and he was recommended to Boyle by Willis; in the treatise about blood warmth Boyle is extensively quoted by Willis; Gassendi also contributed to the nitre theory, and the first mention of nitrous particles (as carriers of coldness, AA 12, p. 44f., cf. 60t) in Willis' works is taken from Gassendi, as well as the concept of an anima ignea, a fiery life-soul, which Willis elaborated in various ways. John Mayow appears to have adopted, in part, Willis' explosion theory (60x) ; he certainly knew Willis' opinions, which he criticized rather sharply.

In his treatise about the accension or inkindling of the blood Willis presents a synthesis of his century's most advanced concepts of metabolism, once more emphasizing an inherent tendency towards an energetic interpretation of natural phenomena. This might be summarized, in present-day terms, as follows: his astonishing notion of a protein-like substance in blood and nutrient humor, acting as a specific building stone of the solid parts of the body, is now completed by the correct assumption of a carbohydratelike substance supplying energy. This energy is set free as heat by oxydation which takes place in the blood; that is why the blood has to be supplied with oxygen through ventilation of the lungs. It is true that this impressive display of anticipations did not lead to the discovery of oxygen as a substance, and had few practical consequences. It is also quite probable that Willis' own contribution to the basic theory of oxygen or nitrous air was not important, except for the problem of the changes in blood color, where he appears to have inspired Lower's successful researches. (cf. above p. 25) But it would not be reasonable to suppose that his essential insights into metabolism had no influence upon his later ideas and discoveries, and upon the strikingly modern outlook which, retrospectively, characterizes the whole Willisian system.

DE MOTU MUSCULARI

In his reconsideration of the problem of muscular movement Willis was less fortunate than in dealing with metabolism. He wrote that even "the most ingenious Steno" abstained from erecting a hypothesis of muscular action upon his findings—which, to Willis, proved the great difficulty of the problems of "animal motive function," but could not keep him from supplying a theory of his own; this is one of the passages where something like a Willisian Daimonion makes its presence felt, clamoring for more and more theories. But here Willis was led astray by his wide knowledge of older authors; he mistook Steno's clear distinction between muscular and tendinous fibres for a proof of the active rôle of the tendinous fibres in contraction. He concluded that insitting or local spirits were staying in the tendons during rest, passing into the muscular fibres and effervescing there together with active particles from the blood, thus stuffing (infarciare) and swelling them and causing a longitudinal contraction upon arrival of a motive impulse from the brain. After contraction these spirits would flow back into their reservoir, the tendinous fibres.

Besides this product of a mesalliance of ideas, the treatise contains a concise representation of Steno's recent findings in muscle anatomy, and a summary of Willis' remaining concepts of neuromuscular interaction. The concept of reflex action is once more explained, and its importance as a cornerstone of Willis' system of theories is made clear; the passage has been called 'the certificate of birth'' of the concept of reflex action by Canguilhem. (111)

In a paper entitled "Willis' place in the History of Muscle Physiology" Hierons and Meyer (182) conclude that apart from the explosion theory Willis' conributions to muscle physiology "have not been of lasting importance" and "cannot be compared to those of Swammerdam, Steno, Goddard and Charleton." This is quite true if his contributions in this field are evaluated outside the general context of his work; however, they were a highly useful constituent of his comprehensive conception of the nervous system: with their help it became possible to erect an advanced theory of convulsive diseases, and to find an ingenious explanation for myasthenia gravis (cf. below p. 166) that is not very far from our modern one.

DE ANIMA BRUTORUM

These "Two Discourses of the Soul of Brutes which is the Vital and Sensitive Soul of Man"* appeared in

*De Anima Brutorum, Quae Hominis Vitalis ac Sensitiva est, Exercitationes Duae. Prior Physiologica Ejusdem Naturam, Partes, Potentias & Affectiones tradit. Altera Pathologica Morbos qui ipsam, & sedem ejus primariam, nempe Cerebrum & Nervosum Genus afficiunt, explicat, eorumque Therapeias instituit.

1672 in Oxford. The book consists of a "physiological" and a "pathological" part. It was reviewed in the "Philosophical Transactions" (124) of May 20th, 1672. The review is a slightly adapted English version of Willis' own preface. We reprint it here because it is easier to read than Pordage's translation. (G)

"What the Learned Author of this difficult Argument had heretofore promised, he now in this Book with much care performeth; which is the Pathology of the Brain, and the Nervous kind, explicating the Diseases that affect it, and teaching their Cures; together with some previous Physiological Considerations of the Soul of Brutes. And because it may, by some, be thought somewhat paradoxical, that he assigneth to that Soul, whereby both Brutes and Men have life, sense, and local motion, not only extension, and as 'twere Organical parts, but also peculiar Diseases, and appropriate Cures; and because also he distinguishes this meerly vital and Sensitive Soul from the Rational, to which he makes it subordinate, and so maketh man a Double-soul'd Animal; he maketh it first of all his business to clear these matters, and to free them from what may seem offensive in them.

In the doing of this he denieth not the Corporeity of the Brutal Soul, esteeming, that both by considerable Arguments, and by very ample, ancient and modern, Suffrages, the same may be evinced; and besides, that its Bipartition is by a necessary consequence deductible from the flammeous Life of the Bloud, and the lucid or Aethereal substance of the Animal

Spirits; both which he hath formerly asserted, and endeavoured to prove. For, if it be granted him, that the Vital portion of this Soul, lodging in the Bloud, be a kind of Fire, and the Sensitive part be nothing but an Agregate of Animal Spirits, diffused all over in the Brain and Nerves; he draws this consequence, That the Soul of a Brute, co-extended to the whole Body, hath not only many and distinct, but also somewhat dissimilar, parts. And if it be objected, that the Soul of a Brute is immaterial, because it perceiveth, or is aware that it feels, Matter seeming incapable of Perception; he answers, That that would be very probable, if that Perception did exceed the bounds of things material, and were of a higher pitch, then what is generally ascribed to Natural Instinct, or Idiosyncrasis: Adding, that none is like to undertake to prove, that the Omnipotent Maker, and First Mover, and Constant Governour of all things should not be able to impress such powers upon Matter, as might be proper and sufficient to perform the functions of the Sensitive life.

And as to what he further asserts, That some people are more, yea sooner and rather sick in their Soul, than in their Body; (whereas Physitians do commonly in Schools refer the principal Seats of all Diseases to the solid parts, and the humors, and vital spirits;) in this he speaketh consonantly to his Hypothesis: For, since that that Soul hath a material Being co-extended to the Body, and peculiar parts, powers and affections, he rationally concludeth, that it is subject to preternatural affections, and frequently needs the Physitians aid.

Besides, he esteems to have made it out in his Pathology, That the Corporeal Soul extends her Diseases not only to to the Body, but also to the Mind or the Rational Soul, and often involves the same in her defects and perturbations.

Moreover, he thinks to have also proved from reason and authority, That there are in Man two distinct Souls, subordinately; and esteems this opinion to be so far from being Heretical or pernicious, that on the contrary he hopes, it will prove altogether Orthodox, and conductive to a good life, and a powerful confutation of Atheism. But to the end that the Author might the better inform his Reader of the Corporeal Nature, and the flammeous and lucid parts, and the affections of the same, he found it necessary both to describe the vital Organs of divers Animals, by whose operation the lamp of Life is maintained; and to represent also te Brains of those they call perfect Brutes, and of Man, discovered by him as to their inmost recesses, and their secret and smallest ductus's. By which manifold and comparative Anatomy, as the manifold and wonderful wisdom of the Creatour is manifested; so are by the same discovered, even in the smallest and most despicable Animals, not only mouths and limbs, but also hearts, being as 'twere so many altars and hearths to perpetuate this vital flame. Here the Reader will meet with very skilful and accurate Dissections of the Silk-worm, Oyster, Lobster, Earth-worm; as also of divers Brains; and first, of that of a Sheep, in a manner excarnated, to make the Medullar streaks, and its inmost fabrick to be seen: And secondly, of a new one of an Humane Brain; where, a Section being made through the falx, the Corpus callosum and the Fornix, and their parts displayed and orderly laid open, are exhibited the streaked bodies, as also the Optick and Orbicular prominencies, etc. That so by confronting these Brains, the vast difference of the Soul of a Brute and that of a Man may the better be shewn.

Concerning the Pathology of this Author, he confesseth, that in delivering the Theories of Diseases he hath relinquish'd the Old way, and produced mostly new Hypotheses which being founded and established upon true Anatomical Observations, give a better account of the Phaenomena of the sick, indicate more aptly the causes of symptoms, and suggest properer waies of curing them. But as to Remedies and his Therapeutical Method, though therein he doth not with others scrupulously insist in the footsteps of the Ancients; yet he rejects nothing that hath been settled by sober Authority, and by long Experience; adding thereunto many things invented by late Experience, and by Analogy. All which he hopes will prove useful both for improving Medical knowledge, and the happier curing the Diseases of the Head; which he enumerates, and discourses upon, both as a Naturalist and a Physitian."

OF SOULS AND OYSTERS

Willis' approach to psychophysical problems seems far-fetched, but in his time diseases of the mind and soul were thought to be subjects for theology and philosophy, not medicine (183) : throughout the world of learning the ancient question (135, 115) whether brutes have souls was a highly popular topic. In the second half of the seventeenth century it became a focal point in the controversy between "moderns" and defenders of tradition. The latter insisted that matter could never have been endowed with the faculty of reasoning, and they upheld this conviction as a bulwark against materialism and mechanism.

In the very year Willis' "Soul of Brutes" was published the question was discussed in a book entitled "Discourse about the Cognizance of Brutes" (184) which appeared in Paris. Its author, a French Jesuit, proposed essentially the same answer as Willis': Beasts do have a sensitive kind of cognition, but not an intellectual one.

Since he was at the same time a devout Anglican, and a fervent *Modern,* Willis attempted to give a solution that could be accepted by the more moderate of both these groups. He made use of the Aristotelian tripartition of nourishing, sensitive, and logical soul (185) . He adapted the formula to the demands of theology, and those of his science. In a similar situation Avicenna had already established a similar formula

(186) , and the tripartite soul had been built into many scholastic systems, especially that of Thomas Aquinas. (cf. 187) . Willis thinks that the higher, or rational, soul is the privilege of Man, being immaterial and immortal; the lower soul, a mortal, and material, body-soul, is the principle of sensitive and basic life in man and beast alike, consisting of a vital and a sensitive part; the sensitive part can have the faculty of reasoning, but only within very narrow limits.

The true enemy of the defenders of the faith was Hobbesian Materialism which denied any qualitative difference between the psychic faculties of Man and beast; Willis was the physician of the Archbishop of Canterbury, and had proved himself a worthy defender of the faith: therefore his compromise was good enough to avoid violent reactions from both sides. Still, Willis said that matter could reason, and the Church did not object: a serious precedent was established, and when some decades later Locke advanced the same concept of reasoning matter in his "Essay", the Church could not recover the territory it had already failed to reclaim from Willis.

In spite of its philosophical and theological claims, the "Soul of Brutes" is not heavily fraught with these arguments. It contains an elaborate psychology of the irrational, a kind of textbook of descriptive psychiatry, about half of Willis' contributions to comparative anatomy, and an account of the senses. Nevertheless the title is not misleading since the body-soul, or "soul of brutes" is the common denominator of these treatises.

Willis gives illustrated explanations of insect organs (taken from Malpighi), of the anatomy of an oyster, a lobster, an earthworm, of three sections of a sheep's brain, and a new one of a human brain, and he discusses characteristics of the anatomy of birds and fish. He wants to show that the apparent diversity of comparable parts in various animals hides their basic identity. The structure of these parts is a key to the ways and means of the "soul of brutes" which he seeks to detect in the various "stages of perfection" in the animal kingdom. He never hints at something like a concept of phylogenetic evolution, but he certainly takes great trouble to provide what amounts to evidence in favour of such a concept.

Cole (106 a) thinks that the "Soul of Brutes" contains Willis' most important work in comparative anatomy. Nowikoff (from Diepgen, 148) has said that the very roots of modern comparative anatomy are in Willis' work about the nervous system.

The "anatomy of an oyster" seems to have made a peculiar impression on Willis' readers. As late as 1706 (188), we meet it again in Leibniz' fictitious dialogue with Locke (New Essays on Human Understanding) as an example for possible uses of comparative anatomy, and as a proof for psychic activity in lower animals. This was affirmed by both Locke and Leibniz, but Locke's disciple, Shaftesbury, made fun of the idea:

he thought that such far-fetched research only proved that the Vertuosi lacked commonsense; he wished to become a new Cervantes in order to do away with this kind of madness as the real one had done with his hero's romances of chivalry. This reminds us of the well-known witticism of Thomas Sydenham, Locke's friend, who said that it was better to read Cervantes than medical literature . . . (189)

Willis' soul of brutes consists of matter in an energetic state: the vital soul is the fire of internal combustion, the sensitive one is the light-like form of the animal spirits in action. This energetic sensitive soul can reach some kind of ratiocination which, however, appears like a drop against the whole sea in comparison with the thinking power of the rational soul. Willis uses his theory of soul to bridge the gap known as the Cartesian dualism. He defines psychophysical relations in a way that resembles a hypothesis which G.Th. Fechner (190) and Wilhelm Wundt (138) formulated about two hundred years later. Wundt says that physical processes are always parallel to psychical ones except for the more complicated psychisms; and Willis believes that the unconscious (or automatic) and the sensory and motor actions are executed by the material soul which has the same extension in space as the body, while the more complex psychisms are the privilege of the rational soul; the rational soul does not control every action of the material soul since it is connected with it only in the gathering-place of the spirits in the middle of the brain . . . The "Throne" and "Capital" of the rational soul is "in phantasia" which is not a physical location, but a functional one. It is there that the rational soul can look at the images which are conveyed through the senses, and represented in the sensitive soul: and there it may give its commands to the sensitive soul.

PSYCHOLOGY

Willis calls the "Soul of Brutes" "our psychology." (EI, 3, p 17) This psychology is built upon an anatomical and physiological groundwork. As has been said, the life-soul is the basic process of life which is combustion in the blood; the sensitive soul consists of the light-like spirits; fire, air, and light are known in mechanics as the most effective and most energetic principles (praecipua ἐνεργετικά). The ingenious structure of the body organs amplifies their efficiency to a nearly supernatural degree. (E I, 4, 23) In "Of Fermentation" Willis defines light as a subtler, and more expanded kind of flame: that means that there is no sharp division between the two parts of the body-soul. This continuity seems to include the rational soul, since in one passage Willis calls the rational soul "divinae particulam aurae", "a particle of a divine breath": he had used the same expression before, in "Of Fermentation", where it glorifies the subtlest of the chemical principles, Spirit; it was adopted from the pantheist, Sebastian Basso. (cf. Lasswitz, 20) It seems that Willis could not always hold on to his theological footing when he was being carried away by the trends inherent in his theories.

The same ideas of continous energetic life-processes have been advanced by psychologists of our time. "If we take our stand on scientific commonsense, and keep away from too far-reaching philosophical considerations, it will be the best thing to understand the psychical process simply as a life-process. With that we expand the narrower concept into the broader concept of a life-energy which comprises the so-called psychic energy as a specification." (C. G. Jung, 139) The sensitive soul is the total of the functional agents of the nervous system, and some of its actions are called "unconscious" by Willis. The sensitive soul has inborn drives of self-preservation, and of propagation of the species. (E I, 5. 28) "Natural determinations" (we would say "instincts") enable it to distinguish that which is useful for self-preservation and propagation from that which is injurious. (E I, 6, 32f) This idea has also been taken up again by psychoanalytic literature. Freud says about the unconscious: "The content of the Ucs. may be compared with an aboriginal population in the mind. If inherited mental formations exist in the human being—something analogous to instinct in animals—these constitute the nucleus of the Ucs." (Freud, 191)

The body soul can combine instincts with experience. Its faculties are perception, imagination, memory, and limited ratiocination. It is capable of cognition. It perceives the sensory impressions, but is not always able to understand them correctly: the sun is just a small disc to the body soul, and the coast recedes from the sailors whose own motion is not realized. (E I, 7, 37) Phantasy is the cognitive faculty of the sensitive soul; it can comprehend simpler things. We can conclude from the behaviour of animals that it must be able to put together or asunder several things at the same time (plures simul componere aut dividere, E I, 7, 37).

Sleep is nothing else but the period of rest of the animal spirits of the cognitive part of the sensitive soul, and that part is the immediate subject of sleep; Willis says that those spirits which come from the cerebellum, and perform the "vital" and "natural" functions which do not become conscious, are not subject to sleep; part of them become more active during sleep, especially those concerned with intestinal functions.

From time to time groups of animals spirits escape the (chemical) bondage of sleep, and roam about aimlessly. They go through the accustomed motions of their waking life, representing thoughts of past events in a confused fashion. This is the origin of dreams: ". . . all of them will not be bound or restrained, but that some of them will walk about the Sepulchers of the rest, like Spectres in a Church-yard, and Cause stupendous Apparitions of things." (E, I, 16, p. 94, quoted from G) Irritations before falling asleep may lead to this evasion of spirits: for instance, agitation, strain, consumption of wine, or tobacco. The spirits in the body organs may also cause dreams: "if the genital humor swells in the vessels, and irritates them, it evokes shameless dreams;" the so-called incubes, or nightmares, result from disturbances in those nerves which stop the movement of the praecordia: that is why we dream that some animal, or a heavy load encumbers our breathing. The witches do sometimes imagine in their dreams that they have visited faraway places, and seen seas and lands unknown to them, which they describe correctly; doubtlessly the devil imprints the ideas of these things so deeply upon their phantasy that they believe for certain to have been there.

Willis believes that dreams originate from spontaneous, and uncontrolled actions of detached parts of the body-soul: most often dreams are only disorderly reciprocations of customary activities of groups of animal spirits. (E, I, 16, 89 f) In this interpretation there is a strong suggestion of automatic unconscious actions facilitated by the absence of conscious control.

The highest part of the tripartite soul is the rational soul, which exists only in Man; its faculties are judgment and ratiocination. "This whole encyclopedia of the arts and sciences" (E, I, 7) is its work, except of course, theology [which is a divine institution].

Willis says, quoting from Gassendi, that the rational soul is connected with the center of the body-soul, imagination, or phantasy which is the function of a gathering of the subtlest spirits in the middle of the brain. There the rational soul governs like a king in his capital. It does not perceive sensory impressions through vibrations, coming from an external shape; it looks at a shape as it is represented in phantasy. (E, I, 7, 39) According to "Cerebri Anatome" imagination is the passive, phantasy the active central function of the body-soul. These functions contain no innate ideas: ". . . nothing is in imagination, or I'd rather say, nothing is in the brain, or heart, which has not been in the senses first."* The body soul is the only link between the material world and the rational soul, and individuals differ in their power of mind not because the power of their rational souls is different, but because their rational souls receive outside information of different quality and quantity. This inequality is caused by inequal brain constitution: in a deficient brain, phantasy will not work well, and it will fail to supply the apparitions or representations which should be worked up by the intellect, or supply them in a distorted state.

Willis goes on in his definition of the rational soul: ". . . but when we will be like the Angels (we may assume), the separated soul will see through every kind of subject with one glance (intuitu simplici), and it will need no corporeal shapes, and no cogitation, in order to detect something hidden in them."** (E, I, 7, 40) This is a description of what has been called mystical consciousness (cf. Stace, 141): a consciousness be-

*. . . nihil est in imaginatione, seu potius dicam, nihil est in cerebro, aut corde, quod non fuit prius in sensu . . .

**. . . quandoquidem erimus sicut Angeli, opinari licet, animam separatam objecta quaevis intuitu simplici perspicere, et nullis speciebus corporeis, nulluque ratiocinio ad detegendum aliquid in iis latens indigere.

yond the sensory and the intellectual. As long as it is dwelling in the body, therefore, the rational soul appears to keep up a state of sensory-intellectual consciousness: this agrees with the rest of Willis' description; he does not explain, however, what happens to the rational soul during sleep.

The cognitive faculty of the rational soul is the intellect, that of the body-soul phantasy, or imagination. The conative faculty of the former is volition, that of the latter, desire. (E, I, 7, 40) Intellect considers the shapes that keep appearing in phantasy, arranging and directing them at will. It also arranges and directs the desires and emotions which move about in phantasy: ". . . it approves of these emotions, rejects others, at times evoking, at times supressing them, or confining them within some right limits . . ."* (E, I, 7, 41) That is, the higher soul, the conscious one, impedes or promotes the actions and passions of the lower soul (which are, in part, unconscious). The lower soul, again, may oppose the commands of the higher one. This will lead to a war between the two souls in one body which will only be ended after one overcomes the other, and takes it prisoner (E, I, 7, 41) The lower soul may also seduce the higher, and corrupt it so that it takes part in empty sensual pleasures. When the rational soul later regains its status and dominance, it may attempt to do penance for its ignominy by self-punishment and mortification of its flesh. (ibid) For

*affectus hos probat, illos rejicit, alios modo excitat, modo compescit, aut in fines quosdam rectos divertit . . .

instance, the body-soul may be bent upon the sexual parts; if it is opposed by the rational soul, the flame of lust (libidinis flamma) can be repressed for some time: "But if the reins of Reason be slackened, or new incentives of lust applied, the corporeal soul shakes off its yoke, and plunges again into similar enormities." (E, I, 9, 52)

Willis speaks of " . . . Sympathies and Antipathies of a diverse Kind, which are as it were proper and intimate Affections, seem to belong to the Corporeal Soul by it self, and abstracted from all Relation . . ." (E, I, 8, 46, quoted from G) The body-soul may be captured not only by beautiful shapes: things less beautiful, even things which most people dislike, may fascinate it, and take it prisoner (velut fascino allectam corripiunt, & captivam ducunt (E, I, 8, 43 f.)), because "the sensitive soul secretly strikes up a friendship with certain things of which the [so] affected are not conscious . . ."* (E, I, 8, 43 f.) Otherwise harmless things are more atrocious to some people than a Gorgon head: the presence of a toad, an eel, a certain dish of meat. ". . . this kind of affect comes, without doubt, from hidden enmities of the sensitive soul . . ." ** (ibid) If the structure of the spirits of the body-soul has been thrown into confusion by an encounter with a certain thing, it will always dread to meet it again. (ibid)

*cujus ratio est, quod anima sensitiva amicitias, quarum affecti haud conscii sunt, cum rebus quibusdam secreto init. . . .

**. . . cujusmodi affectus proculdubio ab occultis animae sensitivae inimicitiis procedunt . . .

Some of these passages come close to the spirit, and even to the letter, of psychoanalytic texts. As in Freudian theories, a conditionally subordinate psychic level may perceive, memorize and act upon informations which remain outside consciousness; there is a censor instance which controls contents passing from the more or less unconscious. Willis had no knowledge of psychoanalytic methods, but he was under continuous pressure from his ever-increasing accumulation of observations which often seemed to defy any attempt to bring them into context, and he had been brought up by teachers whose method consisted of giving everything its place in a universally comprehensive system of learning. Since he had contributed himself to the abolition of that system, he attempted to establish an alternative to it: he could never confine himself to the limits of bare empiricism, and he was too much dependent upon practical observation to be able to create a truly philosophical system with its inherent rigidities. Hence he had to build up his kind of medical anthropology which was flexible and adaptable enough to allow for tentative correlation of seemingly irreconciliable facts and ideas. In his neurophysiological theories this flexibility, and an unusual readiness to adapt ideas to facts, had enabled him to go beyond mere mechanistic interpretations towards the dynamic, and even the energetic; the same advantages now enable him to interpret psychical phenomena in a way that comes close to a psychodynamic view.

PSYCHOPATHOLOGY

Historians of the nineteenth and twentieth centuries have been more interested in the descriptions of diseases in the second part of the book than in the theories about the soul. About 1845, Calmeil (142) gave a detailed account of the "pathological" part. He thought that "the writings of Thomas Wills concerning the different kinds of convulsive affections and concerning the . . . [mental diseases] represent a nearly complete treatise on cerebral pathology. Willis generally excels in differentiating the species of diseases, in expounding the functional disorders that belong to each of them, in localizing the physical alterations which, as he supposes, produce those impairments of health, and in expounding the methods of treatment." In 1928 the "Pathological Part" was again discussed at length by Vinchon and Vie in their essay on Willis' neuropsychiatry (122) ; they concluded: "In spite of inevitable insufficiencies, the impulse had been given, and neuropsychiatry saw the highroad of progress being opened. . ."

Cranefield (115) reprinted and commented the contemporary English version of the 13th chapter of the "Pathological Part": "Of Stupidity, or Foolishness." He thinks that Willis described schizophrenia as something different from oligophrenia. Calmeil (142) already pointed to the fact that Willis found a close relation between mania and melancholia: "they approach each other by the analogy of their nature", and they can change into one another. Willis compared the melancholic and the manic with a burning substance which may emit either smoke or flame; smoke is often followed by an outburst of flame, flame by smoke clouds. We know now, from Willis' diary of 1650 (181), that he actually observed this change during the first years of his practice.

In his essay on the history of Myasthenia gravis, (143) Keynes says that Willis gave the first clear description of Myasthenia gravis, which he calls "extraordinarily precise and well observed;" he thinks that "Willis was familiar with generalized myasthenia and had observed the phenomenon of fatiguability with recovery after rest so characteristic of the disease." Of course Willis could not resist the temptation to try for a theory: "In this kind of spurious palsie arising from the defect, or rather, the weakness of the animal spirits, than their obstruction, it may be suspected, that not only the Spirits themselves are in fault, but besides that sometimes the imbecillity and impotency of local motion doth in some measure also depend upon the fault of the explosive Copula suffused everywhere from the blood into the moving Fibres." (E, II, 9, "De Paralysi", quoted from G) Keynes says that "this looks like an inspired anticipation of the modern theory of the action of acetylcholine. . .". Willis certainly localized the cause of his "spurious palsie" or "paralysis spuria" as a defect in a chemical constituent which is indispensable for the transformation of nerve action into muscle action; the essence of his theory still holds; this proves once more that wrong theories can lead to correct results, and it shows that even Willis' bizarre explosion theory could be a useful tool.—The next description of myasthenia gravis appeared as late as 1877. (Samuel Wilks, cf. Keynes, 143) Keynes thinks that the Erb-Goldflam symptom-complex (myasthenia gravis) ". . . might even more suitably have been called the Willis-Goldflam disease."

In the same chapter on "Paralysis" Willis describes a combination of paralysis and insanity. Vinchon and Vie think that "this passage could place Willis among the clinical precursors of general paralysis", while Kelly (144) and Garrison-Morton (83) think that it is an early description of general paralysis, and Cranefield (115) says it is the first description of the disease which can be positively identified. In the same chapter Willis mentions improvements in insane patients after fevers.

The pathological part of the "Soul of Brutes" contains chapters about headache, disorders of consciousness like lethargus, somnolentia continua, coma, carus, disorders of sleep like pervigilia, coma vigile, incubus; about vertigo, apoplexia, palsies, delirium, phrenitis, melancholia, mania, stupidity, and foolishness—and arthritis and colic. These psychic and somatic disorders are interpreted as results of defective motion or constitution of the animal spirits within the nervous system. Most of these explanations rely upon chemical concepts; Calmeil (142) said that to Willis, the "nervous system of the alienated resembles a kind of laboratory where the effervescence of the liquids, altered by bad ferments, reacts incessantly with the mind, upsetting its equilibrium." He thought that Willis "sins by his liking for explanations, for theories which he would not be able to substantiate by appealing to the testimony of the senses, and which could not always be approved by reason." (142) In the middle of the nineteenth century, Willis' chemical interpretation of cerebral action was an absurdity to Calmeil; but in 1928, Vinchon and Vie wrote that "the humoral equilibries, fantastic as they may have been in Willis' pen, are not any more ridiculous to our eyes. . ." (122). In 1966, results of neurophysiology and psychopharmacology have furnished a new basis for chemical explanations of cerebral functions; by now, Calmeil's view appears rather more absurd than that of Willis, since today's attempts at detailed chemical explanations of cerebral functions are hardly much more substantial than those of Willis, while the feasibility of such explanations has been established beyond doubt.

But Willis does not confine himself to Iatrochemical explanations on the basis of neuroanatomy. At times, as in the 13th chapter on "Stupidity or Foolishness", he uses a method of conceptual description which is not different from that of twentieth century descriptive psychiatry. (cf. 115) Psychic diseases are explained as disorders of the animal spirits, and of the network containing them, the nervous system. That means that the body soul is the seat of these disorders; and the body soul, according to Willis, may also affect the body, and even the rational soul. This idea has been ascribed to van Helmont (Lain Entralgo (103 b) and others) . While such an influence cannot be excluded, since Willis did know van Helmont's writings, we must maintain that the gradual growth of this concept can be traced back through all previous publications of Willis. It appears as a direct consequence of the development of his theoretical system which, as we have attempted to show, began from an eclectic or syncretist platform and not from adaptations of the doctrines of only one teacher or sect. In the diseases of the body soul Willis recommends a broad spectrum of therapeutic measures; the indications depend on the course of the disease, and on the temperament and constitution of the patient. Along with the Iatrochemical medicaments he still uses the herbal concoctions of Galenic medicine, and he "makes use of surgery, physical means, climatology, diets, psychotherapy, and pedagogy. He follows in that the great classic tradition of Galen and Coelius Aurelianus." (Vinchon and Vie, 122)

Willis has often been blamed for his recommendation to beat the mental patients. He actually did recommend beating, but only in cases of unmanageable "mania" where he believed that patients could only be influenced by fear and respect for their keepers. Severe agitated psychoses were obviously beyond his integrating capacity, but we must remember that until Pinel's time they remained outside the field of medical care which Willis had at least helped to extend onto the more readily accessible mental diseases. Besides, "while treatment in the asylums is violent enough, the indications for internment are quite strict, and Willis practised cures without confinement in the most part of his cases." (Vinchon and Vie, 122) Current overrating of the brutality in Willis' methods originates from Calmeil and Semelaigne, who were under the immediate influence of Pinel's great reform. Zilboorg, for instance, says: ". . .he would rather beat a mentally sick man or consider him possessed by the devil than attempt through compassion to gain sympathetic understanding." (133b) This is not only an oversimplification since Willis always tried to replace supernatural explanations of diseases by natural ones (cf. p. 122), and since beating is recommended only once among a vast array of therapeutic measures, while "sympathetic understanding" is certainly not lacking in many passages of the "Soul of Brutes". Misconceptions like the one quoted above seem to have led to some disregard of the book; the reason for them becomes clear if we consider further sentences from Zilboorg: Willis "laid the foundation of a psychiatry without psychology which took root in medical science. . ." (133 b); " . . . the nonpsychological orientation of medical psychology which was so authoritatively established by Willis" (ibid.); ". . . that the brute is but a soulless, mechanical contraption. This contention survived in Thomas Willis and in Descartes." (133 c) These passages can only be explained by complete absence of first-hand knowledge of the "Soul of Brutes"; it has been shown that Zilboorg formed his opinions on other authors, e.g. Joseph Dacquin (146), from second-hand informations, especially from the writings of Calmeil and Semelaigne. Ironically enough, the seventeenth century English translation of the "Soul of Brutes" seems to have been instrumental to the introduction of the very term "psychology" into English . . . (115)

SENSORY PHYSIOLOGY

This theme is amply discussed in Chapters 10 to 15 of the "Physiological Part." The layout follows closely that of Gassendi in his description of the senses. The contents are also partly Gassendian.

The fourteenth chapter, "Of Hearing", contains the first known identification of the cochlea in the inner ear as the primary organ of hearing, and an anticipation of Helmholtz' theory of resonance. "As to the Shell, the use of it seems to be, that the audible Species being brought thorow such turning and winding Labyrinths, and so receiving an augmentation by reflection, and manifold refraction, it may become more clear and sensible; then further, that every Impression, carried about by this winding and very narrow way, may come more distinct to the Sensory: because by this means, care is taken, that many confused Species together, may not be brought in. After the example and similitude of this Shell, artificial Caverns, and arch'd Meanders, wont to be framed by Architects, for the increasing of sounds, and for the distinct propagating of them to a wonderful distance. Further, there is another use of the Shell, no less noted, to wit, that the audible Species may be impressed on the Fibres and the ends of the sensible Nerves, inserted in this place, not at once or at large, but by little and little, and as it were in a just proportion and dimension." * (E, I, 14, 200) (quoted from G)

The same chapter contains the first known description of "a perversion of the sense of hearing in which the subject hears better in a noisy environment." (Schmidt, 145) This is still called "Paracusia of Willis" or Psophacusis Willisii, the only surviving eponyme belonging to Willis besides the "Circle of Willis", and the only memorial to a genuine Willisian discovery in current medical nomenclature. (145; E, I, 14, 198)

SOME CONSEQUENCES

"De Anima Brutorum" is an attempt to make mental diseases a subject of worldly medicine in spite of the fact that "soul" is involved in these disorders; it

*Porro subest alius, isque non minus insignit cochleae usus, nempe ut species audibiles non ἀθρόως sed paulatim, ac velut in justa proportione, & dimenso, nervorum sensibilium, hic loci insertorum, finibus imprimantur.

is an attempt to enforce the competence of medicine in dealing with psychical problems. Willis tries to overcome the inevitable theological preoccupations by means of a device of Scholastic or Aristotelian origin, his "sensitive soul" which he completes with a "vital" soul developed from the fire-soul of Gassendi. (111, 115, 122) The body-soul as a whole becomes a vitalist and animist concept, a formative principle which is alone able to make the step from matter to life. Quite like the "organizator" of today's embryology, it directs developments of the body, and it keeps it from decaying. (E, I, 5, 2 7f)

Most functions of the sensitive soul are irrational, and the functions of the rational, or higher soul depend on them. The rational soul can act reasonably only in the state of sensory-intellectual consciousness: in this state it directs the central processes in the sensitive soul which, on the other side, has to provide the entire material for rational thinking. The irrational, and the unconscious psychisms are related to the rational psychisms in a way that might be called symbiotic. The irrational leads a life of its own which is determinated by the two basic drives, by the instincts, and by the habits of the spirits which keep to the ways they often pass through; it is directed towards the pleasure principle.

The animistic and psychological tendency in the "Soul of Brutes" may be understood as a manifestation of a trend towards replacing chemical explanations by psychical ones, and mechanistic or materialistic thinking by energetic and vitalistic thinking. This trend is represented in the writings of leading Iatrochemists since Paracelsus, and it seems to originate from a reaction against the separation of magic from the chemical doctrines. The same trend appears in a highly irrational shape in van Helmont's doctrine of the archeus, and in a rational and simplified shape in Sylvius' doctrine on spirit. In the "Soul of Brutes" it is cast in a more clear-cut and systematic form, and strongly supported by facts and relevant ideas from many fields of learning. The trend from chemistry to "psychology" in the broadest sense reached its summit in the famous Animism of Georg Ernst Stahl, and Stahl's views originate from Willis and Sylvius, his theory of fermentation (192) is developed out of the Willisian one: Stahl started as an Iatrochemist, and ended in an energetic, vitalistic, animistic soul-medicine. (74c, 60r)

The development of psychologic and psychiatric concepts after Willis has been notably influenced by Locke. John Locke was a friend of Sydenham and Boyle, and a pupil of Willis. His sentence about the difference between idiots and madmen is still quite known (147a) : "In fine, the defect in naturals seems to proceed from want of quickness, activity, and motion in their intellectual faculties, whereby they are deprived of reason; whereas madmen, on the other side, seem to suffer by the other extreme. For they do not appear to me to have lost the faculty of reasoning; but having joined together some ideas very wrongfully, they mistake them for truth; and they err as men do that argue right from the wrong principles; for, by the violence of their imaginations, having taken their fancies for realities, they make right deductions from them." According to Leibbrand and Wettley (74c) this formula was maintained throughout the eighteenth century. In Willis' "Soul of Brutes" the same difference is defined as follows: "Many differences of this Disease are to be met with; and first, there is commonly wont to be a distinction between Stupidity and Foolishness, for those affected with the latter, apprehend simple things well enough, dextrously and swiftly, and retain them firm in their memory, but by reason of a defect of judgment, they compose or divide their notions evilly, and very badly inferr one thing from another; moreover, by their folly, and acting sinistrously and ridiculously, those who are Stupid, by reason of the defect of the Imagination and Memory, as well as of the Judgment, do neither apprehend well, or quickly, nor argue well; besides they behave themselves not as the others by toying and gesticulation, but sottishly, foolishly, or like a dull Ass; so that simplicity of these is the more miserable, who shew so the Disease in their countenance and behaviour."* (E, II, 13, 189, quoted after (G)

Cranefield (115) compares this passage with the psychiatric concepts of Eugen Bleuler. In Willis' "foolishness" he sees an early description of schizophrenia. While this interpretation has a rather narrow basis, the resemblance of Willis' descriptive method to that of twentieth century descriptive psychiatry cannot be denied. However, there is a still closer resemblance between Willis' formula and that of Locke which appeared many years later in the "Essay concerning human understanding"—which had been mentioned first as a project in 1671, about a year before publication of "Soul of Brutes." Of the two formulas that of Willis is obviously a result of accurate clinical observation, whereas that of Locke contains a narrowed-down definition of "Foolishness" which fits only some especially drastic cases thought to be characteristic by the general public, such as the well-known "Napoleons" or Cervantes' famous "Licenciado Vidriera."

Other passages from the "Essay concerning human understanding" (147) also point to the "Soul of Brutes" as their origin. Locke expounds the ancient opinion that nothing can be in the intellect which was not before in the senses (Cicero, Thomas Aquinas). The same is found, modified, in the "Soul of Brutes": ". . . nothing is in imagination, or I should rather say, nothing is in the brain, or in the heart, which has not been in the senses first . . ." (E, I, 8, 46) Locke says: "For, methinks, the understanding is not wholly unlike a closet, wholly shut from light, with

*quod priore [stultitia] affecti, res simplices satis dextre & celeriter apprehendunt, inque memoria firme retinent; attamen ob judicii defectum, notiones male componunt, aut dividunt, & longe pejus aliud ex alio inferunt . . . E contra stupidi, propter imaginationis, ac memoriae, aeque ac judicii defectus, nec bene, nec celeriter apprehendunt, nec bene arguunt . . .

only some little opening left, to let in external visible resemblances, or ideas of things without . . ." (147b) This image is used by Willis in the chapter on seeing, where he compares the eye with a camera obscura fitted with a lens, and in the chapter on the knowledge of brutes, where he defends his notion of a focusing of all sensory impressions through the "sensorium commune" as follows: "I say that this must amaze no one who sees the objects of a whole hemisphere admitted into a darkish chamber through an aperture, and there suddenly depicted most exactly as by an artist's brush: why should it be impossible that the spirits, quite like the light rays, imitate the images or effigies of things by very rapid configurations, and show them without any obscuration or confusion of species?" * (E, I, 6, 31)

Locke stresses the importance of "reflexion", the inner perception of the mind ". . . when it turns its view inward upon itself, and observes its own actions . . . (147c) This concept may also be traced back to the "Soul of Brutes", where Willis uses his original term for reflex action in the same sense ". . . moreover the human mind looks at itself by reflex action, thinks of itself thinking, and hence recognizes its own existence which cannot be perceived

*Dico hoc neminem mirari debere, qui totius hemisphaerii objecta, per foramen in cameram tenebricosam admissa, ibidemque derepente super chartam veluti artificis penicillo exactissime depicta, intuetur: quidni etiam spiritus, aeque ac lucis radii, configuratione citissima rerum iconas, sive simulachra effingant, eademque sine ulla specierum confusione, aut obscuratione exhibeant?

by sense, nor by phantasy . . ."* (E, I, 7, 37) This is not the only instance where Willis anticipated Pawlowian ideas; already in "Cerebri Anatome" the inventor of reflex action had attempted to explain higher psychisms by his new term and concept (memory as reflex action of imagination, above p. 94). However Locke's interpretation of the term "Reflexion" fits quite well into the range of ideas of his former teacher.

Locke says ". . . that sometimes the mind perceives the agreement or disagreement of two ideas immediately by themselves, without the intervention of other: and this, I think, we may call intuitive knowledge. For in this, the mind is at no pains of proving or examining, but perceives the truth, as the eye doth light, only by being directed toward it." (147 d) Locke's use of "intuitive" differs from that of the earlier schools of philosophy (67,etc.), but "intuitus" and "intuitio" appear with much the same connotation in Willis' "Soul of Brutes": ". . . opinari licet, animam separatam objecta quaevis intuitu simplici perspicere, et nullis speciebus corporeis, nulluque raticinio ad detegendum aliquid in iis latens indigere" (E, I, 7, 40); ". . . non perculsione e specie corporea, sed intuitione in ipsam in phantasia expressam. . ." (E, I, 7, 39) Again, the underlying concept is that of reflexion, since the rational soul may realize the representations of things in phantasy "intuitione" because the sensi-

*. . . insuper mens humana actione reflexa seipsam intuetur, se cogitare cogitat, exinde propriam existentiam neque a sensu nec a phantasia percipiendam agnoscens . . .

tive soul represents them "as in a mirror." (E, I, 6, 30f)

The cognitive capacity of brutes in Locke's view is identical with the cognitive capacity of Willis' anima sensitiva: beasts are capable of reasoning, but they can only combine ideas of first-hand objects of the senses, they cannot do abstractions. (cf. above p. 159, and Locke, 147 f) Locke maintains that matter may be endowed with reason, and he defends this contention with the same argument Willis used in the preface to his "Soul of Brutes": one cannot set bounds to God's omnipotency by denying that God could give to matter the faculty of thinking. (loc.cit.,cf.above p. 150) This passage has been underlined in one of Leibniz' copies of Locke's "Essay", together with several other passages which expound Locke's Willisian attitude to the problem of the "soul of brutes." (188) One of Leibniz' more important works, "Nouveaux essais sur l'entendement humain" (188) is a critical discussion of Locke's "Essay" in the form of a dialogue; one of its protagonists, Théophile, who defends Lebniz' own opinion, enters the discussion with a survey of the article on Rorarius in Bayle's famous "Dictionnaire. . ." (188, cf. 135) This article contains a most comprehensive review of the relevant opinions about the "soul of brutes" up to Leibniz. Although Leibniz mentioned Willis as a famous physician, and among the usual list of the leaders of the earlier *"Vertuosi"* (193), and although he knew Willis' physical theories (Lasswitz, 20), he seems to have met Willis' ideas about the soul only indirectly through Locke.

The extent of Willisian influence in Leibniz' monadology is difficult to estimate, but the monadology is something like an infinitesimal calculus of "stages of perfection" of souls, and it can only have been invented on the basis of a less refined theory of subordinate souls: as a starting point, Willis' theory of the tripartite soul would have been more readily accessible to a rational thinker than the inhomogeneous and semimystical ideas of van Helmont. (not so in: Pagel, 194)

Locke's "Essay" is conceived as a psychology of the rational. Locke declines to deal with "physical considerations of the mind", although he concedes that this might be "curious and entertaining." (147e) The irrational in mental processes is something pathologic to him (147h), and he thinks that associations of ideas which do not belong together by their nature (i.e. empirically) are a kind of "madness" (147h) which occurs every day, and in every man, and which must be cured by clear and disciplined thinking. Fear of ghosts, or "sympathies or antipathies" (see above p. 163), are examples of this insanity. As he tries to explain these aberrations he cannot do without physical concepts: "Custom settles habits of thinking in the understanding, as well as of determining in the will, and of motions in the body; all of which seem to be but trains of motion in the animal-spirits, which once set a-going, continue in the same steps they have been used to, which by often treading are worn into a smooth path, and the motion in it becomes easy, and, as it were natural." (147i) With this passage Locke makes use of the concept of "Bahnung" in the brain which has been clearly defined by Willis. (74c)

Locke is interested in those psychical processes which he regards as rational ones. Where he is compelled to deal with irrational processes, he adopts ideas which are already known. In these subjects he follows his former teacher, Willis, whose "Soul of Brutes" supplies a kind of background to Locke's psychology of the rational. Since it was Locke who founded the rationalist psychology of the "age of enlightenment," we have some reason to assume that this school of psychology was under considerable influence by Willisian ideas; we have pointed out possible Willisian influence in Leibniz's work; finally, the animistic theories of Georg Ernst Stahl's system of medicine which became the culmination of the animistic trend in Iatrochemistry probably owe much to Willis' psychologic-theories.

Rather (195) shows that Stahl was not able to find a satisfactory connection between body and soul, between res extensa and res cogitans; nevertheless, Stahl was so much in need of such a connection that he postulated a substantial but incorporeal moving power serving as the "missing link" between body and soul—a vague entity which he did not define more clearly. Rather (195) thinks that he was unable to specify this concept because of the general acceptance of Cartesian dualism, and that van Helmont had been able to disregard this dualism only because he belonged to the pre-Cartesian era. Willis, however, did not belong to the pre-Cartesian era, he knew the pertinent Cartesian doctrines, but he opposed them from an anthropologic standpoint, he was not encumbered by the strict limits of a philosophic system, and he demonstrated that it was possible to build up a good and fruitful working hypothesis of a definite connection between body and soul in spite of the objections of one-track logic. It is highly probably that Stahl did not see any need to "find a satisfactory connection" because Willis had already amply demonstrated that Cartesian dualism was no serious obstacle to psychophysical research.

PHARMACEUTICE RATIONALIS

This is Willis' last work, except for the treatise on the plague which was published posthumously, and is of so little importance, being hardly more than a collection of current beliefs, that I shall give no account of it. (cf. 151) "The Pharmaceutice" appeared in Oxford, the first part in 1674, the second in 1675, shortly after the author's death. Both parts were reviewed in the "Transactions." (124 d) In "Pharmaceutice" Willis attempted to put medical practice on the basis of research; in a last mighty effort he tried to fulfil his dream of a scientific medicine, and failed; but the book became a textbook both of medicine and pharmacology, containing at least one major breakthrough: the first description (in European medical literature) of the sweetness of diabetic urine. (70, 94)

Pharmacology, says Willis, has been studied only

empirically, not scientifically. Medical pharmacology has been confined to combination, dosage and indication of drugs, and no one has explained the influences on the parts of the human body to which the internal and external remedies owe their effects. (F, I, 1, p. 1) It is necessary to establish medicine, as well as "most other sciences and arts", on conclusions from experiments and observations. This is the only way to avoid headless and hazardous treatment and to ward off the all too often justified attacks against medicine. (F, I, preface) In the first place, the more or less mechanic cause of the effects of the medicaments in the body must be investigated. (F, I, 1, p. 2)

The first part of the "Pharmacology" contains an account of the mechanism of vomiting, of the vomitives, and of the remedies against vomiting, together with a description of the anatomy of the organs which are primarily involved; Willis makes use of experiments like intravenous injection, and he concludes that vomitives appear to affect the stomach and esophagus through the brain and nervous system. In the same manner the laxatives, and the remedies against diarrhea and dysentery are discussed, then the mechanism of diuresis, diuretics, excessive diuresis, diabetes and its varieties, remedies against excessive diuresis, or ischuretics, then sweating, the means for sweating (diaphoretics), and against it, then heart affections, and "cardiacs", and finally the "opiates", that is, the sedatives and hypnotics, their dangers, and the necessary precautions in their application.

The second part contains a comprehensive survey of

the respiratory diseases, especially pulmonary diseases, diseases of the liver and the gall bladder, then a discussion of hemmorhage, measures against it, bloodletting, local applications like vesicatories and branding, and a systematic description of skin diseases. Here the descriptions of diseases and their morbid anatomy prevail over therapy.

More recently parts of the "Pharmaceutice" have met with renewed interest. The descriptions of diabetes mellitus, asthma, pleuresy, and cardiospasm have been reprinted—from the contemporary English translation—by Major in his "Classical Descriptions of Diseases." (93b) Canguilhem (111h) has reprinted and translated into French the original Latin text of the chapter on "cardiacs." W. Snow Miller has given a rather detailed account of the chapter on pulmonary phthisis. (149) He reaches the following conclusions:

"1. He [Willis] studied both the macroscopic and the microscopic structure of the lung. As the result of these studies he gave a description of the lung which was superior to any preceding description.

2. He made numerous autopsies and endeavored by combining his clinical with his postmortem observations to obtain a better knowledge of the pathology of the disease, anticipating Morgagni by nearly a century.

3. He carefully observed the effect of the remedies used and formulated a method of treatment which anticipated the modern "open air" treatment of incipient tuberculosis."

As Berdoe (150) says, Willis was the first who attempted to reform the debased state of the materia medica, but today the work as a whole is nearly forgotten. The reason is obvious: the therapy of the "Pharmaceutice" is hardly more lenient than that of most contemporaries of Willis, it makes liberal use of the "Dreckapotheke", of bloodletting, branding, vomitives and laxatives. In spite of several solitary feats like, for instance, the treatment of cardiospasm by means of a specially constructed detrusory, Willis' project of reform remains utopian, and the pharmacological contents of the book are seldom more than a very good survey of contemporary therapy. In spite of "modern" scientific systematism, only rarely a correlation between Willis' results and his therapy is obtained. His therapeutic intentions are for the most part not rational; he "rationalizes" their traditional and empiric foundations, substituting the missing correlations between observations and therapy by means of his chymical conjectures.

But Willis certainly did contribute to a stricter confinement of the indication of these heroic, often senseless, and many times nearly murderous treatments. His reform program probably gave an essential impulse to the development of pharmacology as a science. However, the importance of his "Pharmaceutice" to this development cannot be evaluated with certitude as long as the history of therapy remains an underdeveloped part of the history of medicine. That notwithstanding, the excellent descriptions of diseases place the book among the classics of medical literature.

III CONCLUSION

WILLIS AND HIS SYSTEM

We have found the following basic trends in the works of Willis:

1. Willis was an exceedingly gifted gatherer of data about ill and healthy Man. He was, one might say, possessed with the need to bring them into context. He did this with the help of the scientific methods of his time, to which he contributed some notable advances; but he neglected, or declined to apply, exact quantitative or mathematic methods.
2. He tried to explain his data and the types, or "gestalts" he developed from them, in a *modern* way, condemning the models of explanation of the Galenists and Aristotelians, applying instead terms and theories adapted from anatomists, physiologists (Harvey), chemists and Gassendians.
3. He accumulated these explanations into a system capacious enough to accommodate the numerous contradictions converging in his own person: on

the one hand his traditional upbringing had committed him to scholastic and galenic tendencies which he could not shake off completely in spite of his polemic against them, on the other he followed the revolutionary *New Science* in the method of integration of his results. Contradictions of a similar size arose from the growing struggle between traditionalists and innovators in science, philosophy, religion and politics, since Willis was a personage of high importance in both opposing camps at the same time. Even in religion Willis was forced to reconcile the irreconciliable: in the limited materialism of his "Soul of Brutes" he constructed a compromise between the demands of theology and science which, essentially, has remained a popular loophole for religious doctors up to this very day. This crossing of the Cartesian gap stretched the capacity of his system to the utmost, thereby weakening its inner coherence. The system became universal enough to replace the destroyed traditional system of world and medicine; but because of the same stress his way of correlating gradually lost the appearance of a *scientific* method.

The development of this system may be summed up as follows: Willis is brought up in the scholastic and galenic tradition of Oxford. He is influenced by Paracelsists, probably quite early; later he meets the apostles of experimental natural science who teach him an efficient way to apply his talents of observation and discovery of the typical. In his first book Willis tries to adopt the usage and thought of his scientist friends; under the flag of the *New Science* he brings his Iatrochemical (Paracelsist) notions into rather loose context with his excellent descriptions of diseases, hereby taking part in that reform movement which has been characterized by Virchow (152): "After blood had been recognized in its individuality [by Harvey's discovery], interest in the other humors naturally faded. Hence, by and by, a new humoral pathology arose, which had nothing in common with the old one but its name."

Willis extends this "new humoral pathology" to the nervous system. He investigates the anatomy of the entire nervous system; his results surpass those of his predecessors; probably under the influence of Glisson's and Wharton's doctrine of nervous juice he combines his anatomical results with his chymical ideas. Something entirely new is attained: the combination produces Willis' energetic concept of the action of the animal spirits which, in turn, leads to the invention of the concept of reflex action. Further combination of these fundamentals with experimental, clinical and comparative observations (observations in comparative anatomy, physiology, and ethology) gives rise to a physiology of more complex psychisms. This again is combined, in the final theoretical frame of the "Soul of Brutes", with psychological sentences of ancient and *modern* philosophers and divines. The extensibility of the chymical theories allows for integration of this theory of soul with the results of clinical neurology and psychiatry into a "psychopathology" in the broadest sense.

In this way Willis produces a model, or blueprint, of a comprehensive kind of medicine, backed up on every side by contemporary science. Since it concerns but a part of general medicine, the next step would be an extension to general medicine: this becomes the scope of Willis' last work, the "Pharmaceutice", where he is carried away in spite of his intention to write about therapy, and ends by showing at least some outlines of a Willisian system of general medicine.

Analysis of the development of Willis' theoretical system shows that his successes were not, as some say, simply lucky hits of a fashionable practician who just about dabbled in theories; his theoretical system developed into an utopian model of scientific medicine; its intrinsic laws showed him the way to further discoveries. This model could not fail to produce the same trends that came up again in the last hundred years' scientific medicine, and brought about a tendency to collect and study pathologic phenomena, regardless of their rarity or insignificance, only according to possible correlations. That is why Willis published observations like that of Myasthenia gravis, and for the same reason he was able to concede his failure to find a valid explanation for the sweetness of diabetic urine: he spoke of a problem worthy to be solved (nodus vindice dignus, F. I sect. 4 Chapter 3 p. 67). Again and again he said he hoped later researchers would continue and complete his work, parts of which he called "samples" (specimina). These are not only usages adopted from his Vertuosi friends, nor symptoms of the so called "aversion to final statements" typical of the baroque age: Willis had recognized the misproportion between his means and the size of the problems he was up against (cf. preface to the second part of "Pharmaceutice").

I conclude that not only Willis' inventions, but also his discoveries cannot be evaluated regardless of the development of his theoretical system which produced the necessary "new patterns of discovery." The history of Willis' work is suggestive of philosophical inferences from science like the following: "In a growing research discipline, inquiry is directed not to rearranging old facts and explanations into more elegant formal patterns, but rather to the discovery of new patterns of explanation." (N. R. Hanson, 153)

The same intrinsic laws of the Willisian system explain the paradox that Willis, who was a faithful conservative Anglican, tried to rid his work from the influences of church, religion and superstition.

True, the "Soul of Brutes" has a theological scope, but only so far as it is necessary in order to soothe the zest of the censors of dogmatic purity; retrospectively, the book has more the appearance of a device to keep the divines at bay than that of a contribution to a synthesis between theology and science.

The same tendency to keep religious conservatism

from interfering appears in the remark about the devil's role in epilepsy: since the devil has natural mechanisms at his disposal like, for instance, epileptic fits, he needs no supernatural manifestations to torture mankind. (cf. above p. 122) Here Willis obviously makes use of the ideas of early "liberal" theology—a movement tending more towards Puritanism than Anglicanism. The same point of view applies to Willis' opinion on the belief in witches. Willis' medicine has not much use for this complex of superstitions: following Weyer's line of thought, he attacks the widespread witch-craze, again pointing out that natural causes can explain most seemingly supernatural phenomena. (C 7, s. 43 f., see above p. 160) While Willis is not alone in this attitude—William Harvey, for instance, had contributed to the fight against the witch-craze—it must be remembered that even illustrious members of the Royal Society, like Joseph Glanvill, sook to revive public interest in witchcraft and ghost-lore at about the same time, and that the general witch-panic was still slowly receding since the last great witch-huntings in England had taken place, only decades ago, under the Commonwealth. Apart from these rather critical attitudes to religious questions, Willis' doctrine of souls endangered the simple Cartesian solution which made things so much easier for the defenders of the faith. So Willis had reason enough to profess his loyalty to the Church-line in public: in the dedication to "Cerebri Anatome" he condemned atheism as incompatible with natural science, and in the preface to the "Soul of Brutes" he strove to defend its contents against possible accusations of heresy. Willis was, more or less, a "reluctant enlightener," and he took some trouble to avoid polemic in his relations with the Church. This was made easier for him by his close relationship with the Archbishop of Canterbury to whom he dedicated his works, whom he attended as physician in ordinary, whose case history he was able to publish—by name—in the "Soul of Brutes." (E, II, 8, 142 f.)

DECAY OF THE GLORY

Willis' works became widely known in England and on the Continent. This may be due in part to their quality; other reasons for their success were the reviews in the first scientific journals, sensational controversies, the author's fame as a physician, a "philosopher" and University professor, and as a member of the Royal Society. Each of his works appeared in several Latin editions, and his collected works were reedited sundry times in different places, in Latin and in English. Although Willis did not cause a single major breakthrough which might be compared with Harvey's great discovery, there is nothing comparable to the bulk of his accomplishments in seventeenth century medicine, at least not in England. Willis' life and works contain those features which have been said to amount to the glory of genius. (by Lange-Eichbaum, 155)

III. *Conclusion*

Today Willis is less known even to medical historians than, for instance, Sydenham. This is not a matter of course since Sydenham's medical works do not surpass those of Wills, whom he took as his model, since Sydenham did not contribute any lasting results to basic research, since Sydenham's fame appears to have survived mainly because of the purely empiric attitude he did postulate but could not maintain, and because it is easy to learn from his works.

The posthumous ascendancy of Sydenham over Willis must be considered as part of a major contingency in the development of scientific thinking. Willis' way of integrating observed facts by making use of every suitable idea within reach is characteristic for the whole species of pre-Newtonian scientists, the earlier *Vertuosi,* whose boundless scientific optimism gave them the necessary impetus to overcome their Scholastic adversaries, and made them nearly unable to realize the limits of their projects. Their heroic and often bizarre accomplishments enabled a later generation of students to select those themes, results and ideas which, to them, seemed most important, and to develop them without too much interference from conservative zealots. While Willis' generation had mercilessly done away with the conviction of its scholastic and humanists teachers, the following generation took ample revenge for the "fathers' sins", turning upon the men who had supplied their own leading ideas, the men who had conquered a lasting freedom of research. The

Newtonian generation established stricter standards for the integration of facts, its research projects became concentrated and exclusive, and where the pre-Newtonians had put together aggregates of associations and analogies which remained wide open on every side, the Newtonians constructed more stable, closed systems of logical or mathematical consequences.

Against the Vertuosi ideal of universal genius and universal knowledge there arose the concept of commonsense, as in Shaftesbury's work, the postulate of concentration on the readily accessible among the important facts, as in those of Sydenham and Locke, and the belief in the superiority of mathematics, as in that of Newton. The spectacular universal geniuses, Leibniz and Hooke, were attacked or nearly persecuted by Newton, Sydenham tried to ridicule those who persisted in applying anatomical and microscopical studies to medicine, his close friend and collaborator Locke denounced random association of ideas as a kind of madness, and Locke's pupil Shaftesbury proclaimed the uselessness of studies in subjects such as comparative anatomy. The overall tendency was a simplifying one. The demand was for one-track procedures. Of course the Newtonians were no more able to shake off their whole heritage than the pre-Newtonians had been: as these had continued to use Scholastic, Aristotelian, and deductive ways of thinking along with their new Baconian and Cartesian methods, the new generation brought forth quite a number of potential, or abortive, universal geniuses, among them Locke and

Newton who certainly would not keep to only one field of inquiry.

Sydenham's direct and simplifying way to present his knowledge, his uncomplicated therapy, his abstention from the results of auxiliary sciences, and the lapidary, rugged and unpretentious Latin of his books provided the easily applicable kind of medical information that agreed with the rather frugal mind of the physicians of the age of enlightenment. His aversion against everything not immediately applicable represents an extreme expression of a tendency which can be followed through the history of medicine until today, where it leads to demands for a narrowing down of the preclinical curriculum. (cf. 196) This tendency was diametrically opposed by the Willisian system which corresponds to the broad training in the inductive sciences of most present-day medical schools.

The influence of the strict standards of the Newtonian generation led to a steep decline of Willis' fame, but remembrance of most of his Vertuosi friends was more drastically superseded; Robert Hooke, for instance, merged so completely into the background that by now nobody mentions him as the inventor of the bicycle, and near to no one as the discoverer of artificial respiration, or as one of the builders of London after the holocaust. It has been said that his particular hobby, microscopy, was decisively kept from further development during the seventeenth century by the overwhelming influence of Sydenham and Locke. (197) Evidence for the decline of Willis' fame begins immediately after his death. In the "Transactions" of the Royal Society of 1675, 'Chymistry' " had become now, in the hands of worthy Philosophers, one of the clearest interpretes of the most subtle Abstrusities in Nature"; but in the dedication to the 11th volume, 1676, Henry Oldenbourg says that the "modern Ideas of the Chymists" are now disproved, "since they do not agree with experimental truth." Not much later Francis Glisson repeated an experiment which had been demonstrated in Willis' lifetime by Dr. Goddard, proving that muscle volume does not increase during contraction, contrary to Willis' explosion theory. Dr. Goddard's experiment has been unearthed only 1964 (Meyer, 182), while that of Glisson appears in most pertinent texts of medical history, and hence appears to have commanded far more attention after Willis' death.

Willis' brain anatomy and physiology were attacked again and again since Steno's epoch-making discourse in the house of Mr. Thevenot. It was dealt the final blow by Haller's crudely simplifying doctrine of irritation. (117) So many parts of the Willisian system were made obsolete, actually or seemingly; and the great system could not survive for long in this deprived state, it was soon abandoned and forgotten, while isolated parts still survived. These surviving accomplishments could not save the author's fame since ever fewer people knew more than one or two particulars connected with his name: in Willis' works the relevant passages are everywhere scattered among material that became practically useless, and worse, unintelligible to the uninitiated. Unfortunately Willis' creative genius had developed a rather difficult, though certainly valuable, Latin style which often defies attempts of faithful translation into English, and sometimes contemporary translations lost the original meaning.

As late as 1720, Willis' complete works were reedited in Venice, and they still retained some standing as classics, while his greatest accomplishment, his synthesis, was submerged into the dusts of time under the load of its ever increasing effects.

BIBLIOGRAPHY

WILLIS' WORKS

A Diatribae Duae Medico-Philosophicae, London 1659, Latin. Since this first edition was not accessible, the text from Opera Omnia, Amsterdam 1682, was used. It is identical with that of the Latin edition, Amsterdam 1669.

AA "De Fermentatione," the first part of "Diatribae Duae."

AB "De Febribus," the second part.

AC "De Urinis," the third.

B Cerebri Anatome, London 1664, Latin. The first edition was used.

C Pathologiae Cerebri et Nervosi Generis Specimen, London 1667, Latin. Not accessible; the text of Op.Omn.Amst. 1682 was used; it is identical with that of a Latin edition of Amsterdam, 1668.

D Affectionum Quae Dicuntur Hystericae et Hypochondriacae Pathologia Spasmodica Vindicata, London 1670, Latin. Not accessible; the text of Op.Omn.Amst.1682 was used.

E De Anima Brutorum, Oxford 1672, Latin. The text from

Op.Omn.Amst.1682 was used, but quotations and relevant passages were corrected according to the text of the first edition. In this part of Op.Omn.Amst.1682 there are some misprints that affect the meaning.

F Pharmaceutice Rationalis, Oxford 1674 and 1675 (first and second part), Latin. The text of Op.Omn.Amst.1682 was used, which is identical with that of the first editions.

G Dr. Willis's Practice of Physick, Being the whole Works of that Renowned and Famous Physician . . . London 1684, English. Translated by S. Pordage.

These editions have been compared with: Opera, Lyons 1676; Opera Omnia, Geneva (or: Coloniae Allobrogum) 1676; Opera Omnia, Geneva 1694; Pharmaceutice Rationalis, Den Haag, 1674; Opera Omnia, Venice 1720.

BIBLIOGRAPHY

OTHER AUTHORS

1 Anthony à Wood, Athenae Oxonienses: An Exact History of all the Writers and Bishops . . . Oxford . . . 2nd Edition, London 1721, Vol. II.

2 Joseph Foster, Alumni Oxonienses, 4 vols., Oxford 1892.

3 Dictionary of National Biography.

4 Anthony à Wood, The Life and Times of A. W., Oxford 1891, vol. II - a) p. 325f - b) p. 161 - c) p. 113.

5 James Young, Thomas Willis, in: The New Zealand Medical Journal, 1923, June, XXII, No. 109.

6 Charles Symonds, chapter: Thomas Willis, in: Harold Hartley (Ed.), The Royal Society, London 1960.

7 Letter by Dr. J. Venn, in: S. Weir Mitchell, Some Recently Discovered Letters of William Harvey, Philadelphia 1912, p. 5

8 The Oxford Dictionary of English, 1933, Oxford.

9 Charles Edward Mallet, A History of the University of Oxford, London 1927, vol. III — a) p. 13 — b) p. 66 — c) p. 201 — d) p. 45 — e) p. 46 — f) p. 165.

10 —, Notitia Oxoniensis Academiae, London 1675.

11 Statutes of the University of Oxford, codified 1636; Ox-

ford 1888 - a) p. 62 - b) p. 271 - c) p. 55 - d) p. 41 - e) p. 62 - f) p.39 - g) p. 260 - h) p. 259 - i) p. 36.

12 Phyllis Allen, Scientific Studies in the English Universities of the 17th Century, in: Journal of the History of Ideas, Lancaster Pa. 1949, vol. 10 - a) p. 221 - b) p. 219 - c.) p. 231f.

13 The Hon. G. C. Brodrick, A History of the University of Oxford, London 1886 - a) p. 122 - b) p. 115 - c) p. 114 - d) p. 129 - e) p. 135.

14 Meyrick H. Carré, Phases of Thought in England, Oxford 1949 - a) p. 230 - b) p. 225f. - c) p. 232 - d) p. 250 - e) p. 231 - f) p. 236 - g) p. 243 - h) p. 245ff. - i) p. 273ff.

15 Edward Bagshaw, Exercitationes duae . . ., 1661, zitiert nach Jones (16), p. 147.

16 Richard Foster Jones, Ancients and Moderns: A Study of the Background of the Battle of the Books, St. Louis 1936 - a) p. 8 - b) p. 84 and p. 303 - c) p. 93ff. - d) p. 335 - e) p. 231 - f) p. 316 - g) p. 281 - h) p. 177f. - i) p. 215ff. and 344ff. - k) p. 280.

17 Hugh G. Dick, Students of Physic and Astrology, in: Journal of the History of Medicine and Allied Sciences, I, 2, New York, April 1946.

18 Stephen d'Irsay, Histoire des universités, Paris 1935 p. 107.

19 Marie Boas, Robert Boyle and 17th Century Chemistry, Cambridge 1958.

20 Kurd Lasswitz, Geschichte der Atomistik vom Mittelalter bis Newton, Hamburg and Leipzig, 1890; as complement: R. Hoykaas, The Experimental Origin of Chemical Atomic and Molecular Theory before Boyle, in: Chymia, II, Philadelphia 1949, p. 65ff.

21 Aubrey's Brief Lives, ed. O. L. Dick, London 1958 - a) CIV - b) p. 149 - c) p. 164ff. - d) p. 237f.

22 Encyclopedia Britannica, vol. 10, London 1960, p. 748ff.

23 Andrew Clark (Ed.), The Colleges of Oxford, London 1891: Christ Church, Rev. St. John Tyrwhitt - a) p. 312 - b) p. 314.

24 John Fell [according to Wood (1), (Willis)], Postcriptum from „Pharmaceutice Rationalis" by Willis (in Op. Omn. Venetiis 1720).

25 Willis, Opera Omnia, Amsterdam 1682, „De Febribus", Ch. 14, p. 113ff.

26 Phyllis Allen, Medical Education in 17th Century England, in: Journal of the History of Medicine and Allied Sciences, New York, January 1946, vol. I, No. 1.

27 H. M. Sinclair and A. H. J. Robb-Smith, A Short History of Anatomical Teaching in Oxford, Oxford 1950, pp.11-15.

28 S. Weir Mitchell, Some Recently Discovered Letters of William Harvey, Philadelphia 1912, p. 41ff.

29 Roberti Grovii Carmen de Sanguinis Circuitu, London 1685 [quoted in (28)].

30 Biographisches Lexikon berühmter Aerzte, Wien 1932-33.

31 Montagu Burrows, The Register of the Visitors of the University of Oxford from 1647 to 1658.

32 Wood, Athenae Oxonienses, vol. II, p. 664 [same edition as (1)].

33 Thomas Sprat, The History of the Royal Society of London, London 1667, Facsimile: St. Louis 1959. Notes by Jackson I. Cope and H. W. Jones.

34 Dorothy Stimson, Puritanism and the New Philosophy in 17th Century England, in: Bulletin of the Institute of the History of Medicine, Baltimore, May 1935, vol. III, No. 5. Archiv, Wiesbaden, March 1962, p. 46, vol. I, p. 4ff.

35 Walter Böhm, John Mayow und Descartes, in: Sudhoffs Archiv, Wiesbaden, Marz 1962, p. 46, vol. I, p. 4ff.

36 A Short History . . . (27), Appendix.

37 Wood, Athenae Oxonienses, vol. II, p. 807 (1).

38 R. T. Gunther, Early Science in Oxford, Oxford 1925, vol. III - a) pp. 88-91 - b) pp. 60ff. - c) (diary of John Ward), pp. 60ff. - d) p. 129 - e) p. 96.

39 E. C. Hoff and P. M. Hoff, The Life and Times of Richard Lower, in: Bulletin of the Institute of the History of Medicine, Baltimore 1936, vol. 4, p. 517ff.

40 Autorenkatalog der Zentralbibliothek Zürich (Zettelkatalog), state as of July 1962.

41 Pierre Gassendi . . . sa vie et son oeuvre. Ed. by „Centre International the Synthése“, Paris 1955 - a) Shronologie, pp. 183ff. - b) p. 148f. - c) p. 158 - d) p. 14 - e) p. 68.

42 The Conway Letters (ed. M. H. Nicolson), London 1930.

43 T. S. Patterson, John Mayow in Contemporary Setting, in: ISIS, Brügge, February 1931, vol. XV (I), No. 45 - a) p. 60 (diary of John Ward).

44 Sir Michael Foster, Lectures on the History of Physiology, Cambridge 1901, pp. 270ff.
C. C. Mettler, History of Medicine, Philadelphia 1947, p. 66.
Ch. Daremberg, Histoire des sciences médicales, Paris 1870, vol. II, p. 693.
Puschmann/Neuburger/Pagel, Handbuch der Geschichte der Medizin, Jena 1903, vol. II, p. 346.

45 T. S. Patterson, Jean Beguin and his Tyrocinium Chymicum, in: Annals of Science, London, July 1937, vol. II, No. 3, p. 243ff.

46 The Biographical Treasury; A Dictionary of Universal Biography, London 1876.

47 Camden Miscellany, Camden 3rd Series, vol. 18, London 1948, article: The Restoration Visitation of the University of Oxford and its Colleges (ed. Varley).

48 Robert Plot, The Natural History of Oxford-Shire [first ed. 1677 (30)], London 1705, p. 306.

49 J. R. Partington, The Life and Work of John Mayow, in: ISIS, 1956, vol. 47, pp. 217ff, 405ff.

50 Thomas Birch, The History of the Royal Society of London, 4 vols., London 1754 - a) vol. I, p. 4 - b) vol. II, p. 201 - c) vol. II, p. 217 - d) vol. II, p. 227 - e) vol. II, p. 485 - f) vol. III, p. 242.

51 Henry Stubbe, The Lord Bacons Relation of the Sweating Sickness examin'd, London 1671, Preface to the Reader, quoted in: Jones (16), p. 270f. and note 74, p. 355.

52 Gilbert Burnet, Bishop of Salisbury, History of his own Time, London 1725, vol. I, pp. 285 and 377.

53 Dictionaire des sciences médicales: Biographie médicale, vol. VII, Paris 1825, article: Willis.

54 William Snow Miller, Thomas Willis, in: Bulletin of the History of Medicine, Chicago 1923, vol. III, pp. 215-232.

55 R. S. Dow, not accessible, in: Annals of Medical History, 1940, 2, 181; described with (56) in: Proceedings of the Royal Society of Medicine, Section of the History of Medicine, vol. 55, No. 2, London, April 1962, Section page 11, 287 (108).

56 Sir Charles Symonds, The Circle of Willis, in: British Medical Journal, London, January 15, 1955, pp. 119ff.; cf. Harley, Royal Society (6).

57 Willis, Opera Omnia, Amsterdam 1682, „De Anima Brutorum", Pars Pathologica, 2, 107f.

58 Edmund de Meara, Examen Diatribae; Richard Lower, Diatribae . . . Vindicatio; E. de Meara, de morbis haereditariis; Thomas Sydenham, Methodus wrandi Febres Amst. 1667.

59 Hans Zinsser, Rats, Lice and History, Boston 1935, p. 281.

60 J. R. Partington, A History of Chemistry, London 1961, vol. II: a) p. 172ff. - b) p. 164f. - c) p. 426 - d) p. 177 - e) p. 135 - f) p. 152ff. - g) p. 119 - h) p. 147 - i) p. 202 - k) p. 265 - l) p. 280 - m) p. 274 - n) p. 413 - o) pp. 224, 228, 236ff. - p) p. 304ff. (Willis) - q) pp. 75, 147, 220, 465, 506, 639 - r) p. 684 - s) p. 445f. - t) p. 464 - u) p. 573 - v) p. 574f. - w) p. 550ff. x) p. 587.

61 J. J. Keevil, The 17th Century English Medical Background, in: Bulletin of the Institute of the History of Medicine, Baltimore 1957, 31, S. 523 and: George Urdang, How Chemicals entered the Official Pharmacopoeas, in: Arch. intern. d'histoire des sciences, 1954, VII, 303-314.

62 Phoebe Peck, The Ingenious Author (Dr. Thomas Sherley), in: Medical History (Quarterly Journal), vol. VI, No. 3, London, July 1962, p. 267.

63 Index Catalogue of the Library of the Surgeon-General's Office, United States Army.

64 Catalogue of Printed Books in the British Museum, London.

65 Walter Pagel, Religious Motives in the Medical Biology of the 17th Century, in: Bulletin of the Institute of the History of Medicine, vol. III, Baltimore 1935.

66 Hermann Kopp, Geschichte der Chemie, Braunschweig 1845, vol. I, p. 141 f.

67 Johannes Hoffmeister, Wörterbuch der philosophischen Begriffe, Hamburg 1955.

68 A. Jullien, Topographie de tous les vignobles connus, Paris 1822, p. 423f.

69 Encyclopédie ou dictionnaire raisonné des sciences, des arts et des métiers, par une société de gens de lettres. Mis en ordre par M. Diderot et d'Alembert. Nouv. éd. 36 vol. 3 vol. de planches. 4. Genève 1777-1779.

70 Fielding H. Garrison, An Introduction to the History of Medicine, Philadelphia 1929, pp. 261ff.

71 J. Pagel, Geschichte der Medizin, Berlin 1898.
72 Haeser und Isensee: Emil Isensee, Die Geschichte der Medicin, Berlin 1840, p, 306.
Heinrich Haeser, Lehrbuch der Geschichte der Medizin, Jena 1881, pp. 363ff.
73 Meyer-Steinegg-Sudhoff, Geschichte der Medizin, Jena 1950, p. 320.
74 Werner Leibbrand/Annemarie Wettley, Der Wahnsinn, Freiburg 1961 - a) p. 256ff. - b) p. 274 - c) p. 339 - d) p. 260 - e) p. 314,
75 Johann Hermann Baas, Grundriss der Gesichicte der Medizin, Stuttgart 1876, p. 394f.
76 Kurt Sprengel, Versuch einer pragmatischen Geschichte der Arzneikunde, Halle - a) 4. Teil, 3. Auflage, Halle 1827, p. 353 - b) ibid. p. 201.
77 C. A. Wunderlich, Geschichte der Medizin, Stuttgart 1859, p. 132.
78 Edvard Hjelt, Geschichte der organischen Chemie, Braunschweig 1916, p. 11.
79 Johann Baptist van Helmont, Ortus Medicinae, Amsterdam MDCLII 1652 - a) p. 29f. - b) p. 92 - c) p. 90.
80 Walter Pagel, J. B. van Helmont; Einfuhrung in die philosophische Medizin des Barock, Berlin 1930; and
Walter Pagel, The Religious and Philosophic Aspects of van Helmont's Science and Medicine, in: Supplement to the Bulletin of the Institute of the History of Medicine, No. 2, Baltimore 1944.
81 Sir Charles Sherrington, The Endeavour of Jean Fernel, Cambridge 1946 - a) p. 71 - b) p. 84.
82 Francisci Deleboe Sylvii Opera Medica, Amsterdam 1680 - a) p. 11f. - b) p. 49-51.
83 F. H. Garrison, L. Morton, Medical Bibliography, London 1954.

84 Francis Glisson, Anatomia Hepatis, Amsterdam 1659, 7, pp. 31ff.

85 Carl Oppenheimer, Die Fermente und ihre Wirkungen, Leipzig 1913, vol. I, pp. 6ff.

86 Rudolf Abderhalden, Medizinische Terminologie, Basel 1948, pp. 271 and 303.

87 Ernest Brezina, Medizinisches Wörterbuch, Wien 1948, pp. 145 und 161.

88 William Munk, The Roll of the Royal College of Physicians of London, vol. I, London 1878.

89 Hermannus Boerhaave, Elementa Chemiae, Leiden 1732.

90 Erwin H. Ackerknecht, Zur Geschichte der Malaria. Leber die Geschichte der Malariaforschung, in: Ciba-Zeitschrift, vol. 11, Dec. 52, Wehr-Baden, No. 132.

91 Charles Creighton, A History of Epidemics in Britain, Cambridge 1891, pp. 568ff.

92 C. H. Peckham, A brief History of Puerperal Infection. Bulletin of the Institute of the History of Medicine, vol. 3, Baltimore 1935 - a) p. 192 (Willis) - b) p. 190 (Sennert).

93 Ralph H. Major, Classic Descriptions of Disease, Springfield (Ill.) 1955 - a) pp. 179-181 (Typhoid) and pp.169-171 (Typhus) - b) pp. 577 (Asthma), 628 (Cardiospasmus), 240 (Diabetes mellitus), 571 (Pleuritis).

94 E. H. Ackerknecht, Kurze Geschichte der Medizin, Stuttgart 1959.

95 Nikolaus Mani, Darmresorption und Blutbildung im Lichte der experimentellen Physiologie des 17. Jahrhunderts, in: Gesnerus, vol. 18, 1961, Aarau, fasc. 3/4.

96 K. E. Rothschuh, Entwicklungsgeschichte physiologischer Probleme in Tabellenform, München 1952.

97 K. E. Rotschuh, Geschichte der Physiologie, Berlin 1953, p. 171.

98 Johann Baptist van Helmont, Opera, Lugduni 1667. part: Febrium Doctrina Inaudita, 10, p. 96-97 and 14, p. 101.

99 F. R. Jevons, Boerhaave's Biochemistry, in: Medical History, vol. VI, No. 4, Oct. 62, London, p. 343-362.

100 Fritz Lieben, Geschichte der physiologischen Chemie, Leipzig 1935 a) p. 336, 394 - b) p. 229 - c) p. 656.

101 Thomae Sydenham Opera Universa, Leiden 1741 - a) pp. 48ff. - b) p. 11, 19f., 34, 38ff. - c) p. 20 - d) p. 397, 404, 397 - e) p. 387ff.

102 Johannes Dolaeus, Encyclopedia Medicinae, Frankfurt 1684.
Lorenz Strauss, Palaestra medica, Giessen 1686.

103 Pedro Lain Entralgo, Historia de la medicina. Medicina moderna y contemporanea, Barcelona 1954 - a) p. 225 - b) p. 219.

104 Rudolf Abderhalden, Zur Vorgeschichte der Endokrinologie, in: Ciba-Zeitschrift, Basel, March 1951, vol. 11, No. 124, pp. 4536ff.

105 Jules Soury, Le système nerveux central, vol. I, Paris 1898- a) p. 428-440 - b) p. 438 - c) p. 434 - d) p. 440f. - e) p. 442.

106 F. J. Cole, A History of Comparative Anatomy, London 1944 - a) p. 221ff. - b) p. 10ff. - c) p. 3-4.

107 William Feindel, Thomas Willis . . . The Founder of Neurology, in: The Canadian Medical Association Journal, 87, 289-296, August 11, 1962.

108 Raymond Hierons and Alfred Meyer, Some Priority Questions Arising from Thomas Willis' Work on the Brain, in: Proceedings of the Royal Society of Medicine, vol. 55, November 2, April 1962, Section of the History of Medicine, Section Page 11-16, pp. 287 to 292.

109 Paul H. Kocher, Paracelsian Medicine in England, in:

Journal of the History of Medicine, vol. II, No. 4, New York 1947.

110 Oscar Schmidt, Die Entwicklung der vergleichenden Anatomie, Jena 1855.

111 Georges Canguilhem, La formation du concept de réflexe aux XVIIe et XVIIIe siècles, Paris 1955 - a) p. 74 - b) p. 57-78 - c) p. 68 - d) p. 78 - e) p. 157 - f) p. 169 - g) p. 81 - h) p. 174f.

112 J. F. C. Hecker, Erinnerungen an Willis, in: Archiv für die gesammte Medicin, Jena 1842, II, pp. 441-457.

113 Henry Nigst, Das anatomische Werk Johann Jakob Wepfers, Aarau 1947, pp. 17-20.

114 Hans Fischer, Briefe Johann Jakob Wepfers an seinen Sohn, Aarau 1943.

115 Paul F. Cranefield, A Seventeenth Century View of Mental Deficiency and Schizophrenia: Thomas Willis on „Stupidity or Foolishness", in: Bulletin of the History of Medicine, vol. 35, July-August 1961, No. 4, pp. 291-316.

116 K. E. Rothschuh, Vom spiritus animalis zum Nervenaktionsstrom, in: Ciba-Zeitschrift, No. 89, vol. 8, Wehr-Baden 1958.

117 Max Neuburger, Die historische Entwicklung der experimentellen Gehirn- und Rükenmarksphysioligie vor Flourens, Stuttgart 1897 - a) pp. 7, 8, 2 - b) pp. XXI, XXIII, XXf.

118 Charles Sherrington, Man on his Nature, Cambridge 1951, p. 194f.

119 Heinrich Haeser, Lehrbuch der Geschichte der Medizin, Jena 1881, vol. II, p. 289.

120 C. C. Mettler, History of Medicine, Philadelphia 1947.

121 Carl Oppenheimer, Die Fermente und ihre Wirkungen, Leipzig 1913, vol. I, pp. 6f.

122 Jean Vinchon et Jacques Vie, Un maître de la neuropsychiatrie au XVIIe siècle: Thomas Willis in, Annales Médico-Psychologiques, 86e année, Paris 1928, 12me série, tome 2e, pp. 109-144.

123 J. Lhermitte, Les fondements biologiques de la psychologie, Paris 1925, p. 7-24, quoted in: Canguilhem (111), pp. 152f.

124 Philosophical Transactions . . . of the Royal Society . . ., London - a) vol. I, No. 31, p. 600, London 1668, January 6.

b) vol. IV, No. 54, December 1669, p. 1089: An Account of Nathanael Highmori de Hysterica et Hypocondriaca Passione Responsio Epistolaris ad Doctissimum Willisium, Londini 1670.

c) vol. V, No. 57, March 25, 1670, Beginning the Sixth Year: p. 1178.

d) 1st part of „Pharmaceutice Rationalis", in: vol. VIII, No. 99, December 22, 1673, pp. 6166-6171, 2nd part in: vol. X, No. 121, p. 505 to p. 509, January 24, 167 5/6.

125 Owsei Temkin, The Falling Sickness, Baltimore 1945, p. 184.

126 Glafira Abricossoff, L'hysterie aux XVIIe et XVIIIe siècles, Paris 1897.

127 a) Nathanaelis Highmori exercitationes Duae 1. De passione hysterica; 2. De affectione hypochondriaca, Amsterdam 1660, quoted in 126, p. 36f.

b) Nathanaelis Highmori De Hysterica et Hypochondriaca Passione Responsio Epistolaris ad Doctissimum Willisium, London 1670, summary in: 124b.

128 E. H. Ackerknecht, Kurze Geschichte der Psychiatrie, Stuttgart 1957.

129 Owsei Temkin, Die Krankheitsauffassung von Hippokrates und Sydenham in ihren „Epidemien", in: Sudhoffs Archiv

für Geschichte der Medizin, vol. 20, 1928, Leipzig, pp. 327-352.

130 The Historical Development of British Psychiatry, vol. I, by Denis Leigh, Oxford 1961.

131 Thomas Sydenham, Dissertatio Epistolaris ad Gulielmum Cole, M.D. de Observationibus nuperis circa curationem variolarum confluentium Nec non de Affectione Hysterica Per Tho. Sydenham, M.D., London 1682.

132 D'Arcy Power, John Ward and his Diary, in: Transactions of the Medical Society of London, vol. 40, London 1917, 114th Session, Oct. 9th, 1916.

133 Gregory Zilboorg, A History of Medical Psychology, New York 1941 - a) p. 260 - b) p. 263ff. - c) p. 277.

134 Eugen Bleuler, Lehrbuch der Psychiatrie, 9. Auflage, bearbeitet von Manfred Bleuler, Berlin 1955, p. 447.

135 P. Bayle, Dictionaire historique et critique, 2nd Ed., vol. 3, Rotterdam 1702, article: Rorarius.

136 Wilhelm Hammer, Geschichte der Erkennung und Heilung von Geistes- und Seelenkrankheiten bei Tieren, Berlin, 1928.

137 Peter Scheitlin, Versuch einer vollständigen Thierseelenkunde, vol. 1, Stuttgart 1840.

138 Wilhelm Wundt, Vorlesungen über die Menschen- und Tierseele, 4. ed., Hamburg 1906.

139 Carl Gustav Jung, Uber die Energetik der Seele, Zürich 1928, p. 30.

140 Sigmund Freud, Das Unbewusste, Frankfurt (M) 1960, p. 32.

141 Walter T. Stace, The Teachings of the Mystics, New York 1960, pp. 12-14.

142 L. F. Calmeil, De la folie, Paris 1845, vol. I, pp. 387ff.

143 Sir Geoffrey Keynes, The History of Myasthenia gravis, in: Medical History, vol. V, 1961, pp. 313-326.

144 Emerson Crosby Kelly, Encyclopedia of Medical Sources, Baltimore 1948.

145 J. E. Schmidt, Medical Discoveries, Springfield (Ill.) 1959.

146 Johann Rudolf Nyffeler, Joseph Dacquin und seine „Philosophie de la Folie", Diss. Zürich 1961, p. 4.

147 John Locke, An Essay concerning Human Understanding, Edinburgh 1777 - a) vol. 2, 11, p. 12-13 - b) vol. 2, 11, p. 17 - c) vol. 2, 6, p. 1 - d) vol. 4, 2, p. 1 - e) vol 1, 1, p. 2 - f) vol. 2, 11 - g) vol. 4, 3 - h) vol. 2, 23 - i) vol. 2, 23, p. 6.

148 Paul Diepgen, Geschichte der Medizin, vol. II/1, Berlin 1951, p. 15.

149 William Snow Miller, Thomas Willis and his De Phthisi Pulmonari, in: The American Review of Tuberculosis, vol. V, February 1922, No. 12, Baltimore, pp. 934-949.

150 E. Berdoe, The Origin and Growth of the Healing Art, London 1893. Quoted from Snow Miller (149).

151 Charles F. Mullet, The Bubonic Plague and England, Lexington 1956, pp. 248f.

152 Rudolf Virchow, Hundert Jahre allgemeiner Pathologie, Berlin 1895, pp. 4-5.

153 Norwood Russell Hanson, Patterns of Discovery, Cambridge 1958, p. 2.

154 Henry More, Enchiridion Metaphysicum, Londini 1671.

155 Wilhelm Lange-Eichbaum, Genie, Irrsinn und Ruhm, 4. (ed. Wolfram Kurth), München 1956, pp. 114-151.

156 Le Journal Des Savans, De L'An MDCLXV. Par le Sieur de Hedouville. Paris 1665-67. Karl Sudhoff, Das medizinische Zeitschriftenwesen in Deutschland . . . , in: Auserwählte Abhandlungen von K. Sudhoff. Sudhoffs Archiv für Geschichte der Medizin, vol. 21, Leipzig 1929, pp. 273ff.

157 Heinrich W. Bucher, Tissot und sein Traité des nerfs, Diss. Zürich 1958, p. 25.

158 Kenneth Dewhurst, John Locke (1632-1704), Physician and Philosopher; a Medical Biography, London 1963.

159 Nicolaus Pevsner, Christopher Wren, Paris 1958.

160 Geoffrey Keynes, A Biobligraphy of Dr. Robert Hooke, Oxford 1960.

161 Margaret 'Espinasse, Robert Hooke, London 1956.

162 Robert Hooke, Micrographia, 2nd edition, London 1667.

163 John Evelyn, The Diary of John Evelyn, ed. S. de Beer, Oxford 1955, 6 vols.

164 Charles W. Boase, Oxford, London 1887.

165 M. de Sallaba, Historia Naturalis Morborum, Vindobonae 1791.

166 J. R. Magrath, The Flemings in Oxford, Oxford 1904, vol I, p. 170f., 435.

167 Anthony à Wood, Historia et Antiquitates Universitätis Oxoniae, vol. II, p. 42-43, Oxford 1674.

168 John F. Fulton, A Bibliography of two Oxford Scientists (Lower and Mayow), Oxford 1935.

169 John Richard Green, Oxford Studies, London 1901.

170 Richard Lower, De Corde, London 1669.

171 J. E. Th. Rogers (ed.), Oxford City Documents Financial and Judicial, 1268-1665, Oxford 1891, p. 76ff.

172 F. H. Burgess, A Dictionary of Sailing, Harmondsworth 1961.

173 Thomas Seccombe and H. Spencer Scott, In Praise of Oxford, London 1912.

174 R. C. Churchill, Shakespeare and his betters, London 1958.

175 Kenneth Dewhurst, Willis in Oxford: some new Mss., in: Proceedings of the Royal Society of Medicine, vol. 57,

No. 8, August 1964, p. 682ff., section of the History of Medicine, p. 26ff.

176 Nicolaus Steno, Discours de Monsieur Stenon sur l'Anatomie du cerveau . . . Paris 1669, facsimile in: A Dissertation on the Anatomy of the Brain by Nicolaus Steno . . . Copenhagen 1950, with an English translation from: An Anatomical Exposition of the Structure of the Human Body by James Benignus Winslow . . . Translated from the French Original by G. Douglas, M.D., London 1733.

177 Samuel Brock, Howard P. Krieger, The Basis of Clinical Neurology, Baltimore 1963.

178 Friedrich Albert Lange, Geschichte des Materialismus, reedition, Leipzig 1910, p. 544f.

179 Erwin H. Ackerknecht, Franz Joseph Gall, die Phrenologie und ihre Folgen, in: Praxis, 54, No. 3, p. 71f., Bern 1965.

180 Franz Joseph Gall, J. Spurzheim, Untersuchungen über die Anatomie des Nervensystems, Paris, Strasbourg 1809, p. 27.

181 Kenneth Dewhurst, Thomas Willis as a Physician, Los Angeles 1964.

182 Raymond Hierons, Alfred Meyer, Willis's place in the History of Muscle Physiology, in: Proceedings of the Royal Society of Medicine, vol. 57, No. 8, August 1964, p. 687ff., Section of the History of Medicine, p.31ff.

183 B. P. M. Schulte, Hermanni Boerhaave Praelectiones de Morbis Nervorum 1730-1735, Leiden 1959.

184 P. Ignace Gaston Pardies, S.J., Discours de la connoissance des bestes, Paris 1672, reviewed in (124), 1672.

185 Aristoteles, De Anima, Oxford 1956.

186 Soheil M. Afnan, Avicenna, his Life and Works, London 1958.

187 Karl Vorländer, Geschichte der Philosophie I-III, Reinbek 1963-65.

188 Gottfried Wilhelm Leibniz, Nouveaux Essais, 6. Band der Philosophischen Schriften, Berlin 1962.

189 Pedro Lain Entralgo, Historia de la medicina/Medicina moderna y contemporanea, Barcelona-Madrid-Valencia-Lisboa 1954, p. 220, and:
Chester North Frazier, Heterodoxy and Medical Progress, in: Bulletin of the Hist. of Med., Baltimore, 1946, XX, 1, 58ff: p. 62.

190 Gustav Theodor Fechner, Elemente der Psychophysik, Leipzig 1860.

191 Sigmund Freud, Standard Edition of the complete psychological works, translated by James Strachey, Anna Freud, Alix Strachey, Alan Tyson: vol. XIV (1914-16), p. 195; London 1964.

192 Georg Ernst Stahls Zymotechnia Fundamentalis oder allgemeine Grund-Erkänntniss der Gährungs-Kunst . . . Frankfurt und Leipzig und Regenspurg 1734.

193 Leibniz to Henry Oldenbourg, 29. 4. 1671; Leibniz to Antoine Arnauld, November 1671. In: vol. I of the second series of "sämtliche Schriften und Briefe," Darmstadt 1926, pp. 10, 104, 178f.

194 Walter Pagel, Helmont, Leibniz, Stahl, in: Archive für Geschichte der Medizin, 1931, 24:19.

195 L. J. Rather, G. E. Stahl's Psychological Physiology, in: Bulletin of the Hist. of Med., Baltimore, 1961, 35, January, 1, pp. 37-49.

196 G. A. Harrison, J. S. Weiner, J. M. Tanner, N. A. Barbicot, Human Biology, Oxford 1966: preface (Medawar).

197 David E. Wolfe, Sydenham and Locke on the Limits of Anatomy, in: Bulletin of the Hist. of Med., Baltimore, 1961, vol. XXXV, No. 3, pp. 193ff.

198 Alfred Meyer and R. Hierons, A Note on Thomas Willis' Views on the Corpus Striatum and the Internal Capsule,

in: Journal of the Neurological Sciences, Amsterdam, 1964, 1: 547-554.

199 Alfred Meyer and Raymond Hierons, Observations on the History of the "Circle of Willis," in: Medical History, vol. VI, No. 2, April 1962.

200 Alfred Meyer, The Thirty-Fourth Maudsley Lecture: Emergent Patterns of Mental Disease, in: The Journal of Mental Science, vol. 106, No. 444, July 1960, pp. 785ff.

201 Alfred Meyer and Raymond Hierons, On Thomas Willis' Concepts of Neurophysiology, in: Medical History, Vol. IX, No. 2, April 1965.

202 Kenneth Dewhurst, Dr. Thomas Sydenham, Berkeley 1966.

INDEX

INDEX

INDEX

INDEX

INDEX

INDEX

ILLUSTRATIONS

Baccalaureus medicinae in Oxford. With this promotion the license to practice was usually granted. (Willis: 1646). (Oxonia Illustrata, D. Loggan, Oxford 1675. Zentralbibliothek Zürich)

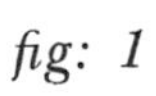

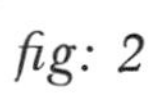

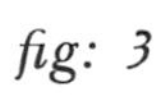

Doctors of medicine in Oxford (Willis: 1660). (Oxonia Illustrata)

Beam Hall, the house near Merton College in Oxford in which Willis lived from about 1649 to 1666. In this Hall the Anglican Church Services, forbidden by the Puritan Rulers, were secretely continued. Thus, this Hall became the spiritual citadel of the University tradition. (After a sketch by John Chessell Buckler, 1821, reproduced in "Bodleian Picture Books", volume: Drawings of Oxford, by J.Ch.B., Plate 13; Zentralbibliothek Zürich)

Sir William Petty (1621-1675). One of the leading pioneers of the empirical Natural Science in England, Universal Genius, among other things Professor of Anatomy in Oxford. In the latter capacity he worked together with Willis. Also, as Chemist he probably exercised some influence on Willis. (A History of the Teaching of Anatomy in Oxford, Oxf. 1950, Table 4)

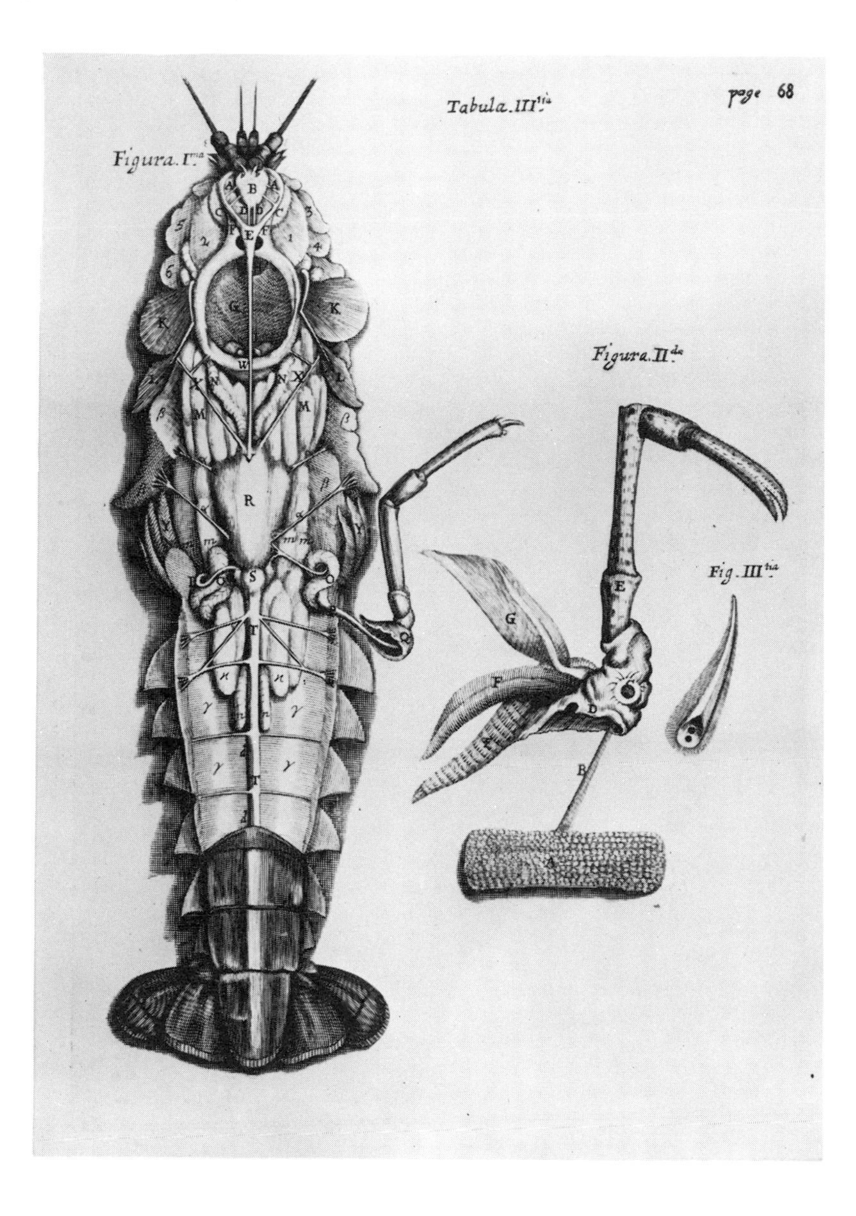

Crayfish (De Anima Brutorum, Willis; 1st edition, Oxford 1672. Institute of the History of Medicine, Zürich.)

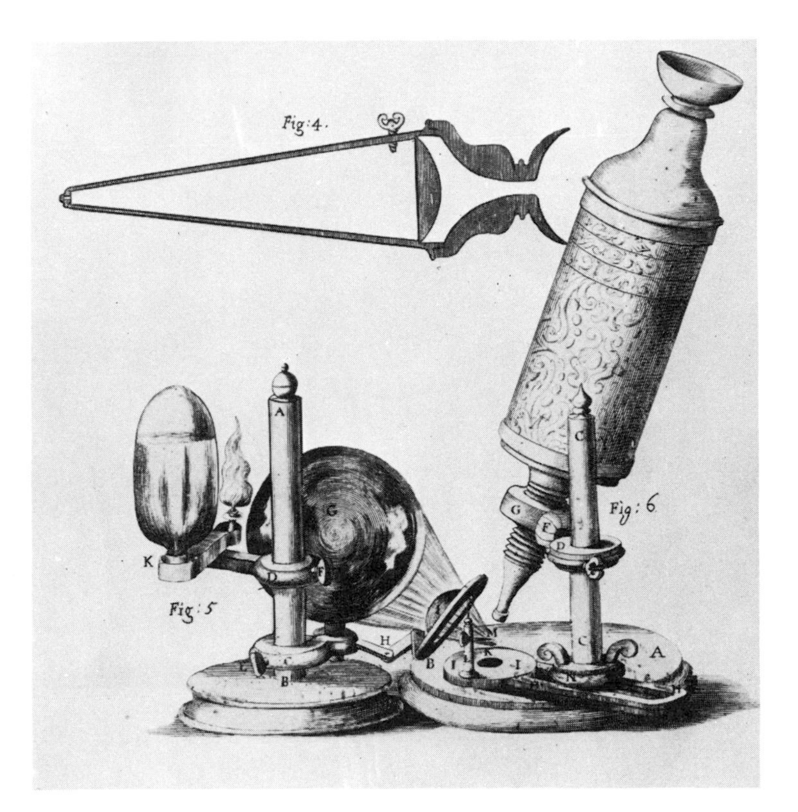

A microscope used by Hooke, a student of Willis. (Hooke: Micrographia, 2. ed. London 1667, Zentralbibliothek Zürich)

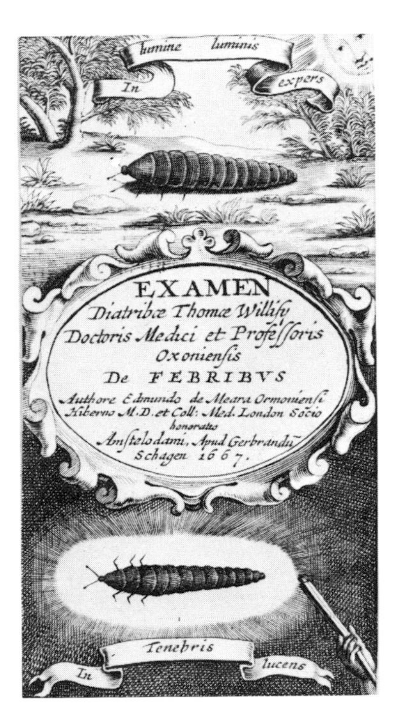

Frontispiece of DeMearas Critique on Willis' work about fever (from the original [58]). Also Frontispiece of an edition done by the same publisher of Willis' "Diatribae Duae". On the title page for DeMeara: "In the light bereft of light, in darkness luminous". On the Frontispiece for Willis: "Thus, things are lighting lights with the help of things" i.e. material objects put light to each other: an allegory for inductive reasoning. This explains the frontispiece for DeMeara as a rather abusive allegory denouncing the obtuseness of (DeMeara's) deductive, scholastic reasoning. (Zentralbibliothek Zürich)

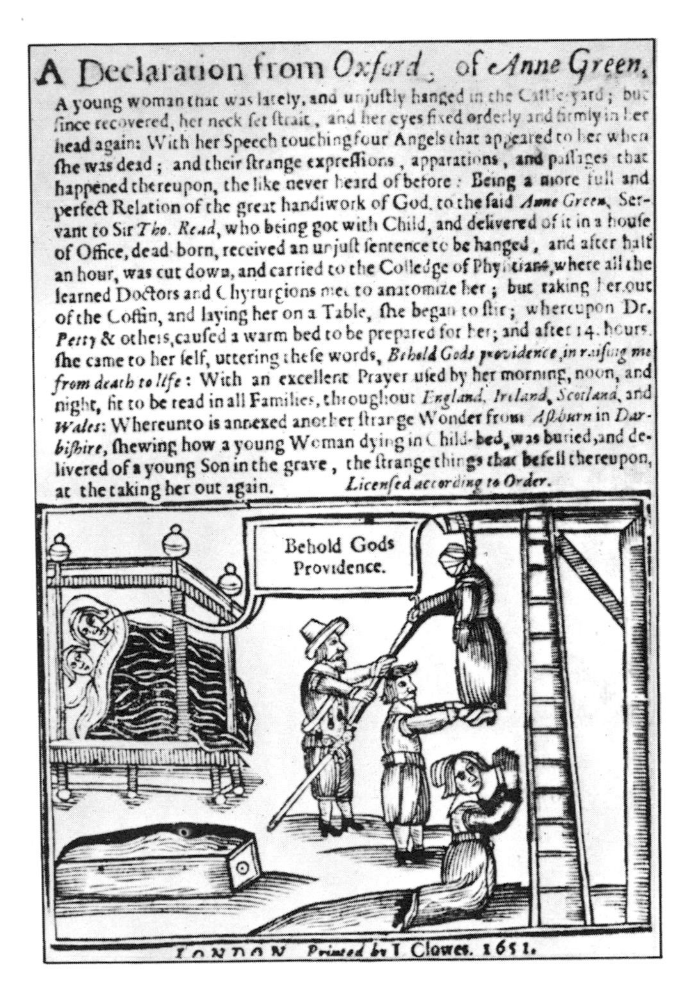

A Declaration from *Oxford*, of *Anne Green*,

A young woman that was lately, and unjuſtly hanged in the Caſtle-yard; but ſince recovered, her neck ſet ſtrait, and her eyes fixed orderly and firmly in her head again: With her Speech touching four Angels that appeared to her when ſhe was dead; and their ſtrange expreſſions, apparations, and paſſages that happened thereupon, the like never heard of before: Being a more full and perfect Relation of the great handiwork of God, to the ſaid *Anne Green*, Servant to Sir *Tho. Read*, who being got with Child, and delivered of it in a houſe of Office, dead-born, received an unjuſt ſentence to be hanged, and after half an hour, was cut down, and carried to the Colledge of Phyſitians, where all the learned Doctors and Chyrurgions met to anatomize her; but taking her out of the Coffin, and laying her on a Table, ſhe began to ſtir; whereupon Dr. *Petty* & others, cauſed a warm bed to be prepared for her; and after 14. hours ſhe came to her ſelf, uttering theſe words, *Behold Gods providence, in raiſing me from death to life*: With an excellent Prayer uſed by her morning, noon, and night, fit to be read in all Families, throughout *England*, *Ireland*, *Scotland*, and *Wales*: Whereunto is annexed another ſtrange Wonder from *Aſhburn* in *Darbiſhire*, ſhewing how a young Woman dying in Child-bed, was buried, and delivered of a young Son in the grave, the ſtrange things that befell thereupon, at the taking her out again. *Licenſed according to Order.*

LONDON Printed by I. Clowes. 1651.

Pious treatise about the raising of the seemingly dead Anne Green with the help of Petty, Willis, Bathurst and others. (A History of Teaching of Anatomy in Oxford, Plate 4)

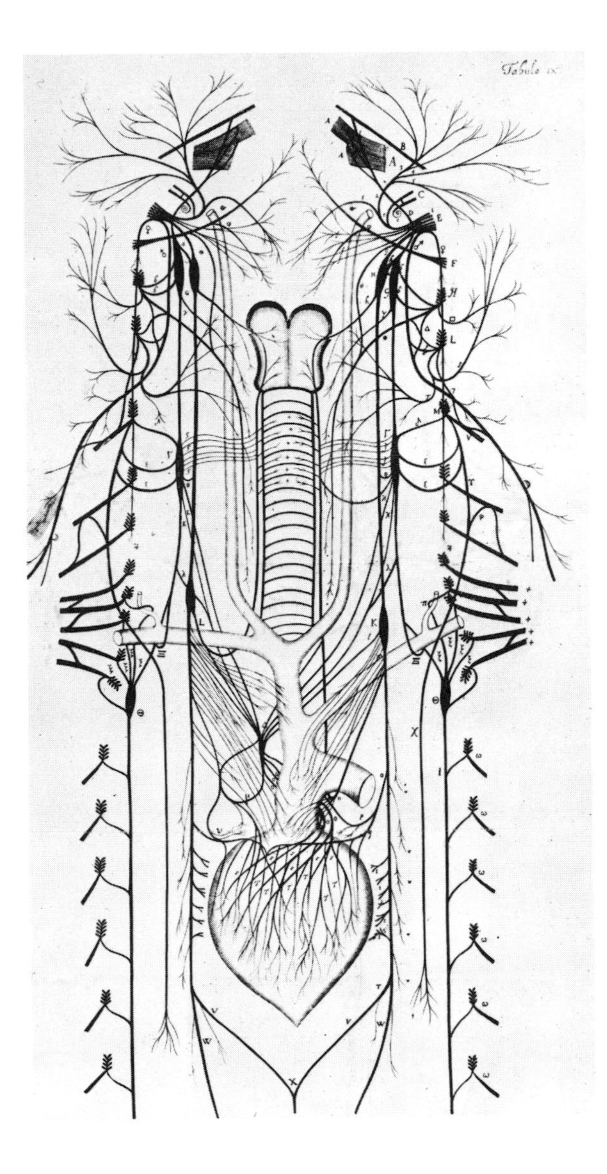

Schematic presentation of the vegetativ nervous system of Man showing the difference between that of man and of other living creatures. (Willis, Cerebri Anatome, 1st ed. London 1664, Plate 9, Plate 10 would be the corresponding presentation for animals i.e. mammals). The sketch was made by Lower. (Institute of the History of Medicine, Zürich).

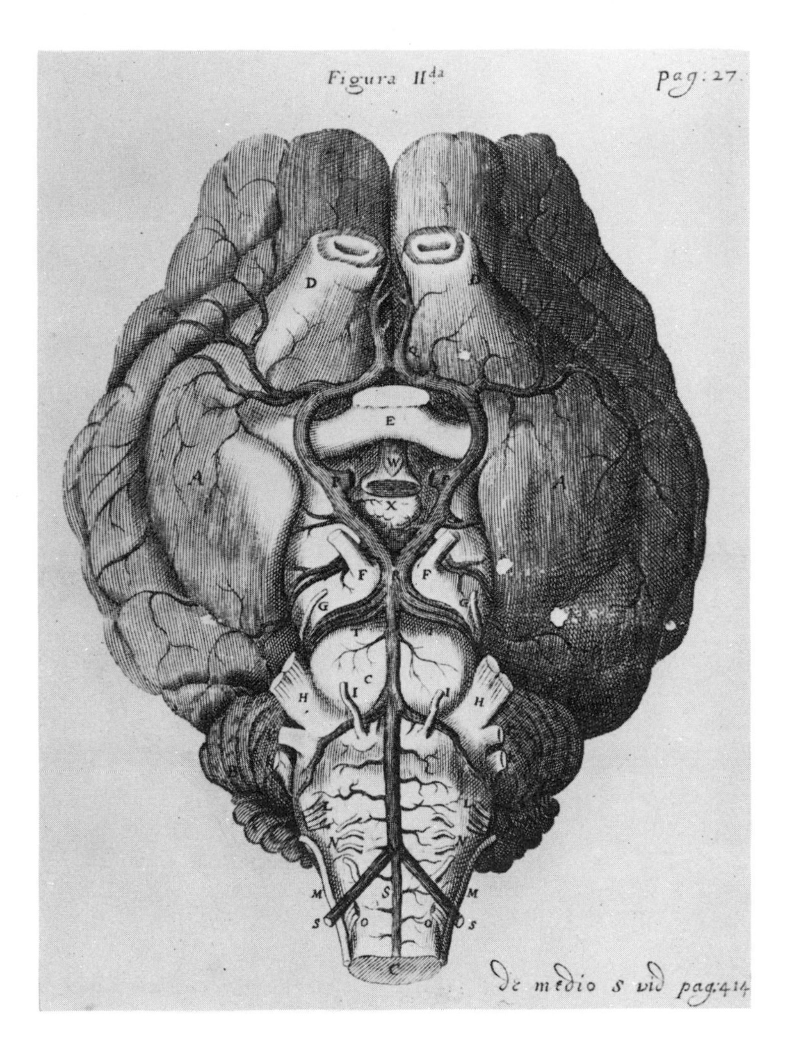

This illustration shows the base of the brain of a sheep and the roots of the cutoff ducts. The arteries had been injected with a black dye, so that they could be seen more clearly (Willis: Cerebri Anatome, 1st ed. London 1664, Plate 2 p. 27 . . . .)

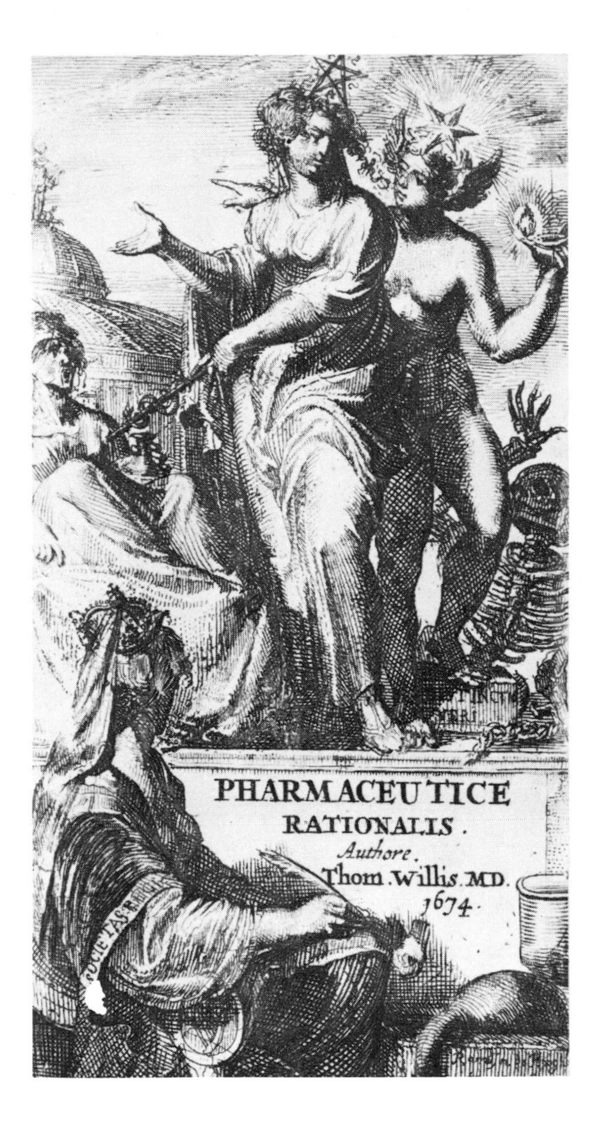

Title page of Duodecimo edition of "Pharmaceutice rationalis" which appeared in the same year as the first edition published in The Hague by Arnold Leers. (Zentralbibliothek Zürich)